THE CRINAN CANAL at ARDRISH...

D0198645

£2.95

Butterfly

HITHER, thither, whither,
  Flitting where you please,
Whither, thither, hither,
  Playing with the breeze.

Darting over purple ling,
  Skirting iris tall,
Resting on a sun-kissed rock
  By the waterfall.

Wings hardly folded,
  Till they're spread again,
Skimming over cotton flowers
  On the thyme-strewn fen.

Up and down and over,
  Round and in and out,
Dancing on a sunbeam
  Near a water spout.

Fluttering above the muddy bank,
  Then suddenly hover,
Silent as the gentle breeze,
  That wafts the scented clover.
                    — *Katherine MacIntyre.*

People's Friend Annual

●

CONTENTS

WEDDING BELLS For Barbie

WHEN Barbie was born, Carol Fallon read every book on child care that she could lay her hands on, and the suspicions that had entered her mind after the separate births of her other children, Justin, Andy and young Harry, were finally confirmed.

She came to the conclusion that, no matter what theory she found regarding child-rearing, it was always possible, by reading a sufficient number of books, to find the theory disproved and discounted as useless by another equally well-qualified child specialist.

Therefore, finding that it was almost impossible to be proved wrong, she threw the books in the dustbin and proceeded to bring up her brood on a couple of principles which seemed sound enough to her. They were quite simple.

Firstly, that children should be led and not driven, and secondly, that they don't always really want the things they demand, or if they do, they don't want them for long.

**Complete Story By
IRENA DICKMAN**

7

Thus, playing it by ear and by rule-of-thumb, Mrs Fallon managed to bring up a relatively stable bunch of children who, though noisy, didn't whine and didn't wheedle, but made their requests in a straightforward manner. Subsequently she found that their lives were not spoilt by the lack of ponies, Irish wolfhounds, sailing boats and trips to the Antarctic.

It was, perhaps, too good to last.

Barbie, at sixteen, got enough pocket money and managed reasonably well on it. She was excused any chores other than picking up her clothes from the bedroom floor because she was studying for "O"-levels, and she was no more secretive than any other child of her age. If she had a request to make, she made it.

She was sitting at the kitchen, watching her mother ice a birthday cake for Andy when she said idly:

"Mum, when you're sixteen, you can get married, can't you?"

Carol Fallon, icing a tricky border round the bottom of the cake, simply said:

"Yes, I suppose so."

"I'm sixteen," said Barbie casually but thoughtfully.

"Yes, I know," Carol answered, "you had your birthday in April and you . . ."

The icing tube slipped from her fingers on to the floor and she looked at her daughter a little wildly.

"What's going on?" she demanded.

"I'm sixteen and I want to get married," Barbie said.

CAROL, afterwards, was always grateful that she never voiced the reason for the sudden fear that gripped her heart like an icy hand. She stared at Barbie, but the child's eyes were limpid and innocent.

No, Carol thought, her heart warming to life again. No, not Barbie. I would know if she were.

"To whom, might I ask? I mean, to anyone in particular? Or is this simply a general idea in your mind?"

"Oh, Mum, of course there's someone in particular. It's Bob!"

"*Bob!*" Carol exclaimed. "Who, for heaven's sake, is Bob?"

"Bob Conrad. *You* know. You said you liked him."

He had been there twice and Carol remembered a tall, lanky boy with a mournful face like a basset hound who ate a whole almond tart baked for six people, and explained the principle of the internal combustion engine throughout each evening.

"And how old is . . . er . . . Bob?" she asked.

"Oh, he's heaps older than I am — seventeen."

Carol picked up the icing tube and wiped it thoughtfully and with elaborate care. She held in her mind, like a charm against evil spirits, her belief that children should be led and not driven, and that if you are subtle about it, you can show them that they don't really want what they ask for, at all she had to be clever about it.

But she retreated into cowardice.

"You're both rather young," she said. "I'll have to talk with your father."

"You won't make me change my mind," Barbie said ridiculously. "We're in love and when you're in love, you get married, don't you? This isn't like being twelve and dying for a pony."

Perhaps we haven't been so subtle, after all, Carol thought.

IT wasn't, from Donald Fallon's point of view, the ideal evening for walking into a family crisis. The advertising firm he worked for had lost a major client that very day, and it had been put to him as senior sales director to find another client.

He brought home a bulging briefcase and had only time to rest it on the hall table when Carol seized hold of his lapels, brushed his cheek with a worried kiss and told him such sketchy details as she knew herself.

He looked at her sourly.

"It's a pity convents have gone out of fashion," he said. "I suppose we could lock her in her room until she's twenty, but the neighbours might get to hear of it, and we'd have the welfare authorities around our necks. Who is this boy, anyway?"

"I *told* you," said Carol impatiently. "Bob Conrad. He's about ten feet tall, six inches broad and thinks Rembrandt is a make of motorcycle."

"Keith Conrad's son?" Donald brightened perceptibly. "She's picked the right family, anyway."

Keith Conrad had been a devilishly daring, desperately young RAF pilot when he first knew him, and the youthful adoration had never completely died.

"Oh, Don, do be constructive. This is serious, you know. You can't drive children. You can only lead them. If we forbid them to see each other, they'll meet secretly and that'll lead to — well, the kind of trouble we most want to avoid."

"Hasn't happened already, has it?" Donald asked, showing either that he was a realist, or that he knew less about his daughter than her mother did.

"Don, how can you think such a thing about Barbie?"

"I don't know," he said gloomily, pouring himself a large and unaccustomed whisky. "I'm looking for a reason, I suppose. We'd better go and see Keith tonight and talk it over."

They were late back from Keith's, but not too late for Barbie to be waiting for them, her face a mixture of mulish expectation and pessimistic hope which could only be achieved by a sixteen-year-old intent on marriage.

"Barbie," said Carol. "Let's go into your room and talk, shall we?"

She held out her hand to her daughter, and they went up the stairs together. Donald, by pre-arrangement, abdicated from his parental responsibilities in favour of finding a new client for the advertising agency.

It would help no-one, he pointed out wisely, if the agency were to go out of business, because he was too old to get another job.

Sitting on the bed beside Barbie, Carol began.

"We've all discussed this pretty thoroughly," she said, "your father, Bob's father and I. And because you're both so young, we feel that we've got the right to make a few conditions. No, don't interrupt. Listen to what I have to say first.

"You're over sixteen — almost sixteen-and-a-half. When you're seventeen, we've decided that you can become engaged officially, with a ring, a party and everything. And when you're eighteen you can be married."

"But, ooh, Mum . . ." Barbie stopped, as her mother's words sank into her consciousness. "Mum . . . really engaged? Properly engaged?"

Carol nodded.

"Slap-up party and everything," she promised. "Everybody there."

"And now, just until then, I'm engaged-to-be-engaged?"

"Whatever that might mean."

OH, Mum, don't be dim. It means engaged-to-be-engaged. I can wear a ring, not a proper ring, but a ring. *You know.*"

"I suppose I do," Carol said doubtfully. "All right, you can be engaged-to-be-engaged. But this isn't the only condition.

"You see, obviously when you get married, you're going to have somewhere to live, and even a tiny flat costs money. So Bob is going to get a job and save money, so that you will both have something to start on."

"Oh, he's got one already," Barbie said readily. "In Charlie's Garage. He's going to work all weekend and most evenings and right through the holidays, and save all the money. And I'm going to work, too."

"*We* have a plan for you, too, dear," Carol cut in smoothly. "Marriage isn't easy for young people, you know, and money's always short — not that we wouldn't help you in a crisis, you know that — but it's essential for you to learn to manage, keeping a nice home going, and cooking proper meals, and all that.

"Now, *we* think that the very best way for you to learn is to take over part of the household chores from me, because experience is the best teacher, after all. I think that if you could take over the cooking and look after the boys, I could manage to pay you, say ten pounds a week.

"But only if you do the work properly, mind, because fair's fair."

"Ten pounds." Barbie's eyes sparkled. "Mum, that would be

super. I could help Bob with his savings and buy things."

"Then it's a bargain?"

"Of course it's a bargain, I could do it with one hand tied behind my back."

"There's one other thing," Carol added. "Bob's dead set on getting his degree in mechanical engineering, and he'll get a grant. Well, I expect you plan to work for the first few years, and nobody's going to look at you if you don't have a decent education.

"Helping in the house doesn't excuse you from working for your exams, any more than Bob is excused school work because he's going to work in a garage."

"Oh, Mother," exclaimed Barbie with exasperation. "We've got it all planned. We've talked it over for hours and hours, and decided on

▶ *over*

FAMOUS WOMEN

MARY SHELLEY (1797-1851)

An English writer, who has a place in literary history as the author of "Frankenstein," she was the daughter of William and Mary Godwin and the second wife of Percy Bysshe Shelley.

Mary came as near as any woman could to meeting Shelley's requirements for the partner of his life: "One who can feel poetry and understand philosophy." After his death in 1822 she published his "Posthumous Poems" (1824) edited his "Poetical Works" (1839) with long and invaluable notes, and his prose works (Es says, Letters from Abroad, etc., 1840).

"Frankenstein," or "The Modern Prometheous" (1818) is perhaps the most widely-known pseudo-scientific novel. Its style is immature but the basic idea is facsinating: the power of the scientist to form and give life to a human being and the dreadful consequences which this act produces.

The treatment of psychological and social problems is extraordinary, the more so in that the book was completed before Mary's twentieth birthday.

She went on to write many more books and devoted the rest of her life to educating her only son. She died in London in 1851.

11

..g that you've just said, only we never thought of the house , which is a *fabulous* idea. It's all just the way we wanted it. ..onestly, it is."

Carol, nonplussed, rose to her feet.

"Very well," she said. "You can start tomorrow evening. I'll get out all my old cookery books and you can do toad-in-the-hole, which is easy. And then you can put the boys to bed. You may as well start as you mean to go on."

"Can I still see Bob?" Barbie asked anxiously. "I mean, you're not going to try to keep us apart?"

Carol looked into her daughter's shining face, and suddenly felt ashamed. You can wave to him in passing, she thought, and then despised herself a little for being glad they'd both be so busy.

"Of course we're not trying to keep you apart," she said.

Downstairs, she said to Donald, "It's going to be all right, you know. I give them three months."

Donald looked up briefly from his lists of likely companies.

"Don't count on it," he replied. "Those kids might surprise you."

THE toad-in-the-hole was not an unqualified success, because it didn't rise in the middle, but it was a fair first effort. Donald Fallon said so.

"I've eaten worse," he said.

"Not in this house," Carol cut in sharply.

"In the company canteen."

After stewed apples and custard (the custard only slightly lumpy) Barbie cleared the table, washed up with the loss of only one old cracked plate and came back to say firmly to the boys:

"All right. Everybody upstairs for baths."

Justin, the eldest, looked at her with open contempt.

"Over my dead body," he said.

Barbie fixed him with a look.

"You're *all* going up to the bathroom," she said firmly, "and the last one up gets a cold shower."

They went, mumbling to themselves, and the sound of the running hot water was drowned by the most appalling series of screams. Harry, who was always tardy, had qualified for the cold shower.

"Children should be led, and not driven," Donald murmured, looking up at the ceiling.

"I've always longed to put young Harry under a cold shower, myself," Carol said stoutly.

The bathing finished, Barbie came downstairs, got out her school books with a series of loud shuffles and bangs which could not be ignored, and settled down to her homework.

By the end of the week, several things had been established.

Barbie had a light pastry hand, she was a natural-born cook, and apparently only needed five hours sleep.

12

She had a stand-up fight with twelve-year-old Justin, gave him a black eye, and was now the undisputed leader of the house.

Her class test results were good, and she settled easily into a domestic routine which enabled her mother to put her feet up in the afternoon for the first time since her daughter was born.

One evening Bob called round.

"Coming to the pictures, wench?" he demanded.

"Barbie," Carol called from the sitting-room, "you've got all that ironing to do for the boys and yourself, you know."

Barbie made a face. "Sorry, no pictures," she said meekly. "Come and keep me company in the kitchen."

A FEW days later Carol found Barbie leafing through the old grocery receipts.

"Mum, we spend an awful lot on food, don't we?"

"We're a big family, and a big-eating family. Perhaps I'm not as careful as I should be, but your father isn't exactly in the poor house and his job's pretty safe."

"Even so —" Barbie's expression of worry did not lift. "Mum, if I could reduce the bills by five pounds a week, would you give me half of it? You'd still be two-fifty to the good."

"I don't know," Carol wasn't happy about this. "I like you to have good food. It doesn't do to be undernourished."

"Oh, Mum, let me try. I've read a book about household economy and another on proper diets. We wouldn't go hungry. *Honestly* we wouldn't. It would only be different food."

Carol looked into her daughter's bright, eager face and gave in. We can try, she thought. We can only try, but what your father will say, heaven only knows!

What Donald said was: "Is it really possible that mince can be cooked in so many ways? Only a completely devious mind could enclose it in suet crust and call it 'Devon Pudding'."

"But it's tasty," Carol said. "You must admit that. It's always tasty."

"Oh, certainly. But you can shape it like a leg of lamb, and serve it with mint sauce, and it's still mince."

But perhaps he knew better than Carol how to deal with Barbie. One Friday evening, he came back home with a brown paper parcel oozing blood that contained three pounds of silverside.

"Dad," Barbie cried aghast. "How could you? It must have cost a fortune!"

"It was given to me," Donald said stoutly. "It was given to me by a butcher — a humane individual who hates to see grown men cry. Keep it until Sunday, cook it and be thankful."

But the following Wednesday, he looked at his breakfast and rose up in horrified wrath at what he saw.

"Barbie," he said tightly. "I am a grown man, and I do a hard day's work. Just because I don't dig ditches doesn't mean to say that I don't need a good, nourishing breakfast to carry me through.

"And to me, at eight in the morning, nourishment means bacon and eggs, give or take a mushroom or tomato or two. I need protein, do you understand? Not this . . . this . . ." He waved his hand at the food, and words, at last, failed him.

"But, Dad, this is protein!" Barbie protested.

"That is a selection of the coldest, most blatant carbohydrate that I have ever seen. I wouldn't feed it to a canary!"

"Dad." Barbie's voice took on that elaborate patience with which the young instruct their elders. "Protein is composed of lots of amino acids, some of which are found in different kinds of carbohydrate. If you select your carbohydrates carefully, you can get all the amino acids at one meal, and that's the same as having protein. Well, isn't it?

"So, if you eat cornflakes, wheatmeal bread and peanut butter, it's just the same as eating bacon and eggs. Really it is. That's how they feed people in under-developing countries."

"I have been developing myself and my stomach for forty-two years," Donald Fallon said deliberately. "And I consider any step in your direction retrogressive. I'll just have coffee, thank you. Thank heaven there's a buffet car on the train."

Carol, overhearing, laughed, but was worried just the same. This was one more problem to add to the other problems, to add to Donald's refusal to take an allotment so that they could grow their own vegetables, (marrows, said Barbie, made the very cheapest jam) and his refusal to allow Barbie to cultivate the same allotment, on the grounds that there were only twenty-four hours in each day and she had already bespoken twenty-five of them.

THAT evening, Carol had a talk with Don because, as she said, it couldn't go on, or Barbie would be a physical wreck.

Donald listened with complete attention — he was still suffering from the breakfast episode — and then went to the bottom of the stairs and called Barbie down.

"Barbie," he said, "you have proved to us that you can be the world's most economical housekeeper and can feed a family of six only slightly inadequately on two-and-a-half pence a week.

"This is extremely laudible, although I sincerely hope that you will never be in the financial position to have to keep it up for any length of time.

"However, we do feel that this concentration on the side of economics makes you — shall we say — a one-sided cook. There is a great deal more to cooking than making mince. I therefore suggest that I enrol you in a cordon bleu cookery school — for which I will pay all expenses — so that you can get an idea of the finer side of gastronomy."

14

Then, as Barbie started to interrupt, he held up his hand for silence.

"Since a cordon bleu is obviously worth more than a common-orgarden cook, the pound that you gain by cheeseparing us into starvation will be added to the money your mother gives you, which will still be added to your allowance.

"During the holidays, you will attend a day cookery school, and then you'll have to make do with evening classes. *I* have spoken."

As Barbie danced out, Donald winked at Carol.

"If you can't beat 'em . . ." he said.

"Don, it will cost a fortune."

"I'll find the money. I'll mortgage the house, sell my premium bonds . . . anything. Just as long as we get some decent food into the house, and never let us have mince again."

Carol picked up the pullover she was knitting for Justin.

"All the same, I do admire her tremendously," she said slowly. "I admire them both. Keith Conrad was telling me that Bob banks every penny of his money, does *two* jobs, and still hasn't fallen behind with his school work.

"With the first money she earned, Barbie bought sheets, and she's hemstitched them by hand. Heaven knows how she found the time, but the stitching's exquisite. I really think we will have to withdraw our opposition to the marriage."

"I know," Donald replied. "We set them impossible tasks, and they've won through. They've behaved like responsible adults, and I suppose we'll have to treat them as such. You know what I've decided to do?

"I'm going to give them a year's lease on a nice little flat as a wedding present. I'm going to get them off to a good start, because I think they deserve it, and I'm proud of both of them."

"And I'll help furnish it," Carol said cosily. "Don, do you realise that it's only twelve weeks away?"

"What's only twelve weeks away?"

"Barbie's seventeenth birthday. The official engagement party. I wonder what they'll want — a formal do with speeches and toasts to

Nature's Hide-Aways

THIS is my lovely private world of
grass, and trees and sky,
Not far away, on busy roads, the cars
are hurrying by;
But here in this secluded spot, where
nature still holds sway,
Wild flowers bloom, running wild in
glorious disarray.

There must be places just like this in
every busy town,
Unspoilt and quiet, narrow lanes for
folk to wander down.
All wild and lonely places hold peace
beyond compare,
And anyone who really seeks will
always find it there.
— *Georgina Hall.*

the happy couple, or very loud music and loads of hamburgers?"

"Hamburgers. Mince. Ugh!" Donald replied.

B ARBIE sopped up cookery as a sponge sops up water. The comestible pattern of the household changed, and the food became gorgeous and, as Carol had feared, terribly expensive.

Carol actually perched herself in the kitchen to watch her daughter, and learnt a great deal about cookery that she never knew before. Occasionally, if Barbie was in a good mood, Carol was allowed to help with a few simple little jobs.

"Do you know what Coulibac is?" Barbie demanded one afternoon.

"It's a tree, isn't it?" Carol replied.

"That's Coolibah," Barbie said scornfully. "Coulibac is an absolutely wonderful Russian fish dish, with a whole fish in brioche dough and I'm going to make it for tonight."

She had an incredibly large, and very dead fish on the draining board. She began to make the brioche dough very quickly and expertly.

"Barbie," Carol said. "What about your party? It's less than a month away."

She raised her head and looked at her mother. "*What* party?" she asked.

"Your engagement party. Remember? You'll be seventeen and you're getting engaged to Bob."

"*Who*?" Barbie shaped the dough in her hands, lovingly and carefully, cutting it into a kind of flower.

"Bob Conard. Barbie, for goodness' sake, listen to what I'm saying!"

Barbie filled a jug with warm water, measuring it carefully.

"Actually," she said. "Bob and I aren't engaged-to-be-engaged any longer. We haven't been for quite a while. About three months, I think."

She dropped the dough into the jug and the coarse petals spread as the dough sank to the bottom.

"Oh, we may marry some day. We're still very good friends. We may marry when we're about thirty. We'll both be pretty well established by then."

And that, thought Carol bitterly, will give us plenty of breathing space.

"Established as what?"

"When I get my cordon bleu, I can get a job as a commis chef in a frightfully good restaurant called the Three Graces. Later on, I'm going to open a little place of my own — very smart and quite small, a dozen tables, and terribly expensive."

Barbie looked severely at her mother. "Mum, if you don't watch what I'm doing, you'll never learn to make Coulibac. I won't always be here to cook for you, you know."

A ND there I was," Carol said to Donald later, after the remains of the feast had been cleared away. "With that damn dead fish staring me between the eyes, running around following Barbie's orders as if *she* were my mother, and I was a sixteen-year-old girl!"

"Which is really what hurts, if you're being honest," Don replied. "Because, after all, you set out to stop this marriage by devious means, and stop it you did."

"And I felt really mean every moment of it. I felt mean because Barbie couldn't go out and couldn't see Bob, and because she worked so hard. I really hated myself, and all the time it turns out that she was doing exactly what she wanted to do."

"Well, she isn't getting married at eighteen, and that was the object of the exercise, wasn't it?" Donald stated.

"But we'd changed our minds about that. We'd just decided that it was a good idea, after all. Oh, I was just getting all steamed up, and thinking how wonderful she'd look in white."

"You'll see her in white," Donald said, not without a trace of gloom, because he had been seeing Barbie as a very young bride, too. "Chef's cap and apron. Oh, come now, darling, hasn't it really all turned out rather splendidly?"

Carol was silent for a moment and then said slowly, "Don, do you think we drove her to it? We've always been so careful to lead the children and *not* to drive them. Would she have made this decision if we hadn't made her take up the household responsibilities?"

"Probably not. She wouldn't have realised her potentialities. But that's something we'll never know. Perhaps leading is only a sort of reverse driving, the same thing under a different name. I don't know.

"If we never lead and never drive, perhaps we're abdicating our responsibilities as parents."

He stood up. "I wonder what cold Coulibac tastes like," he added, going towards the door.

"Oh, Don," said Carol in despair. "You're no help to me at all."

He reached the door, and grinned back at her.

"Take me to your driver," he said.

She threw the newspaper at him, but it bounced off his retreating back. She was annoyed at her lack of success, but then she laughed, and afterwards she found a smile lingering on her lips. Suddenly everything seemed just fine. □

A Gift From The Past

by ALICE CHETWYND LEY

THE only passenger in the compartment was a woman in her sixties, still attractive, dressed in a suitable adaptation of the latest fashion and with well-styled grey hair.

As the train pulled up at the station, she stood up to reach down her case from the rack. She wasn't getting off until the next stop, some twenty minutes ahead, but she always liked to have everything ready.

She placed the case beside her on the floor and was about to resume her seat when the compartment door was flung back vigorously and a young man erupted into the carriage, almost knocking her off her feet.

"Oh, I say, sorry!" he apologised, steadying her with his free arm. "I didn't see you in time — so sorry — hope I've not hurt you."

She murmured that it was quite all right, and sat down.

He tossed his kit-bag on to the rack, taking a seat in the opposite corner. They studied each other for a moment in idle curiosity, as passengers frequently do. He found himself thinking that she wouldn't have been a bad looker when she was young. After a few minutes, he unfolded his newspaper and forgot about her altogether.

But she continued to look at him, cautiously at first and later without really seeing him at all. He was wearing RAF uniform, and would be just about the same age as Richard had been when they first met.

IT was so long ago. 1940, a grey year for England, though seldom before had the skies been so blue or the sun so warm, even in August. Against the backcloth of those blue skies, the Battle of Britain was being fought, and people talked uneasily of invasion.

Susan first saw Richard Brent in the hospital where she started her training. At the time, he was trying to race another patient down the length of the ward. As both young men were on crutches, recovering from leg injuries, the race caused a good deal of amusement.

Bets were being laid by the other patients when Sister Martin intervened.

Sister Martin was the terror of the ward, one of the real old school. The juniors insisted that she'd bleed Dettol if ever she did cut herself, and their favourite joke was that she even starched her knickers. On this occasion, she unbent so far as to pass a comment on the race to the two young nurses who were there.

"Mad!" she said. "Completely mad! These RAF boys are all the same. Still, we can do with their particular brand of madness these days . . ."

Before they could think of an answer, she'd recoverd her usual manner, and sent them scurrying off on some task.

The fair young man spoke to Susan when she was serving supper in the ward.

"Lovely toasted cheese again, Nurse? Sure we don't get more than our ration? I wouldn't like to deprive anyone else — after all, we've only had it fourteen times in the last three weeks."

"It's good for you," she said, trying to look severe. "Lots of protein."

His blue eyes twinkled at her. "No use trying to baffle me with science, Nurse. I never could enthuse about the things that are good for me. But you're new here, aren't you? I haven't seen you before."

She nodded and moved quickly away, as Sister's eye was on her. Later on, when she was helping to clear away, he asked her name.

"Susan Drew," she answered shortly.

"Mine's Richard Brent. Susan . . ." he added reflectively, "it suits you. How long have you been a nurse, Susan? You don't look a day over seventeen."

"As a matter of fact, I'm twenty." Her tone wasn't encouraging. For one thing, she liked to be thought older than she was, not younger.

"Oh dear." He put on a comic look of dismay. "I see I've offended you, Nurse Drew. I'm sorry. Of course, you're really much older than you look, and must have led a fascinating life. Perhaps you'd like to tell me all about it sometime — how about tonight? They expect us to settle down here at nine, and I always did like a bedtime story. Come to think of it, I sleep better with someone to hold my hand, too."

"Really?" Susan put on her sweetest smile. "I'm sorry, I'd like to help you, but I go off duty at eight. Still, I'll ask Sister if you like. I hear she's very good at holding patients' hands."

"While they apply the thumbscrews, I suppose?" He grimaced. "All right, Nurse, you win this time."

A T first she thought he was a bit fresh, and decided to give him a wide berth. But very soon she saw that it was just his light-hearted way with everybody. He even tried it on with Sister Martin, but was soon put in his place.

Once Susan had realised this, she was quite ready to join in his nonsense, though she always kept a weather eye open for Sister's frown.

20

All the same, it was surprising how much she and Richard Brent managed to learn about each other over the next few weeks. Richard told her he was twenty-two, and lived in Somerset with his parents in a rambling old house. He'd been training as an architect but when war came he joined the RAF.

"We'll build some decent houses when the war's over," he said, his eyes alight with enthusiasm. "Not these squalid places you see now in the town, but something with light and air, uncluttered. Schools, too — no more of those dreary prisons that need artificial light all day long. It'll be a new world, Susan —" his voice took on a more serious note — "for those who'll be here to see it."

IT was from someone else that she learnt he had recently been shot down, and nearly lost a leg. He said nothing to her of his exploits. She told him shyly about herself — that she was an only child and lived with her parents in a pleasant London suburb.

"I always wanted to be a nurse," she said. "When I was little, I used to practise on my dolls."

"Better make the most of it, now that you've got some human guinea pigs, then," he teased. "I for one am hoping to get my discharge soon — not that I don't trust your nursing, Susan, but apart from that, I can't wait to get out of here. Sister Battle-Axe says I can take a stroll in the grounds tomorrow, to get my sea legs again. Can't you arrange to be out there, too?"

She smiled, shaking her head.

"Oh, come on, Susan," he urged. "I want to talk to you."

He made an impulsive movement towards her, then remembered where they were, and drew back. "Please, Sue," he said softly.

"I'll try, but I can't promise," she said hurriedly, one eye on Sister.

It turned out to be easier than she had dared to hope. She was actually instructed by Sister to accompany Richard to the quadrangle on the following afternoon.

The short journey taxed his leg, and he was glad to slump on to a bench under some trees in the quadrangle.

"Chestnuts," he said, pointing at the green spiky cases on the branches. "There'll be loads of conkers, later — I'd have given anything, once, for a haul like this. Queer, isn't it, to think that boys have been collecting conkers since goodness knows when, and will probably go on doing it long after we've gone? It's a consoling thought, somehow . . ."

She nodded in quick understanding.

"It's a kind of link between past, present and future — a continuity —" He broke off. "I expect you think I'm mad."

"No, I don't." Her eyes were soft. "I sometimes think like that myself — I expect it's the war — everything's so uncertain, isn't it?"

"Do you?" He reached out and took her hand. "I think we'd feel the same way about lots of things, Sue."

She drew her hand away, looking anxiously at the windows of the ward, which faced this way. "I mustn't stay," she said, turning to go.

A T any time an air-raid siren made her stomach turn over, but now it held a special menace.

She heard the drone of a low-flying plane overhead, and heard Richard shout a warning which she couldn't catch. Then she heard another sound, rapid and metallic, rather like someone typing on a very old machine. It was the first time she'd ever heard machine-gun fire then, and she didn't realise what it was.

"Sue! For goodness' sake, lie down!" He leapt towards her, bearing her to the ground and sheltering her with his body. Overhead, a second drone joined the first, and suddenly the air was vibrant with short, sharp bursts of gunfire. Richard raised his head, watching as a newly-arrived Spitfire chased the solitary raider away from the hospital and out over the horizon.

"Susan, are you all right?" He rolled over, releasing her, and turned her face anxiously towards his.

Susan managed a shaky smile. "Yes, I'm all right, but what about you? Your leg —"

"Oh, Sue!" He drew a deep breath, and gently touched her cheek. "If anything had happened to you, darling —"

"Richard —" Suddenly, she felt the tears starting. She put up her hand to brush them away, and he caught it in a strong clasp.

"Are you two hurt?" They came out of their own world to see to their embarrassment that they were the centre of a group of nurses and ambulance men who'd run towards them. Susan jumped up at once, dusting down her apron to hide her eyes, while willing hands helped Richard to his feet.

"My God, that was a close thing!" said one of the ambulance men.

For the rest of the day, everyone in the ward seemed bent on talking to them about their lucky escape, giving them no chance for any private conversation together. Susan wondered if Richard found this as frustrating as she did, and wished she knew the answer.

In front of the others, his manner towards her seemed the same as always, light hearted and friendly. There was no trace of the tenderness he had shown when danger had threatened her.

Her frustration was increased the following day. Sister Martin told her to report for duty to D Ward until further notice. There was no chance of a word with Richard before she went.

The windows of the new ward also faced the quadrangle, and each day she saw him out there, so near and yet so far.

As the days passed, she noticed he no longer sat on the bench but walked round the quadrangle with the aid of a stick. Soon he scarcely leant on this at all.

Once or twice she caught him looking along the rows of windows. Was he searching for her? She ventured a wave once, but he didn't seem to see.

On the fifth day, he didn't appear in the quadrangle at all.

She felt desperate. Could there be a fresh complication to his leg? She had to find out.

WHEN she reached the Nurses' Home, she sought out Daphne Taylor. Daphne worked with her on Sister Martin's ward.

They chatted for a while before Susan brought up the subject that really interested her. She tried not to be too obvious as she asked a casual question about Richard.

"Flight Lieutenant Brent? Oh, he's been discharged — went today, as a matter of fact."

"Discharged!" Susan couldn't disguise her dismay. "But wasn't it a bit sudden?"

"Yes," Daphne replied, looking thoughtfully at her. "I suppose so,

▶ *over*

FAMOUS WOMEN

GRACE DARLING (1815-1842).

On the morning of September 7, 1838, the luxury steamship "Forfarshire" struck on the rocks near the Longstone Lighthouse, of which her father was the keeper.

Seeing a few survivors, and considering the seas too treacherous for the mainland lifeboat, Grace and her father managed to row the mile from the lighthouse in their coble, and by a combination of daring, strength and skill to rescue four men and a woman.

Her father then returned with two of the men to take off the remaining four survivors.

Grace won nationwide fame, she and her father were given the gold medal of the Humane Society and large subscriptions were collected for them. But she remained at the lighthouse, and died of tuberculosis at Bamburgh aged only twenty-seven.

23

but it usually is, isn't it? They only decided when they did the rounds this morning. He'd been pestering them to let him go for days. Someone came to collect him at two o'clock. No, I've no idea where he's gone — home, perhaps. I know it wasn't back on active service, because I heard Sister say he was to take another few weeks off first. He'll always have a limp, but it won't stop him flying — I heard him telling Mr Stringer, in the next bed."

She hesitated a moment. "He asked me where you were," she went on. "I think he'd have liked to say goodbye to you. He liked you quite a lot. You liked him, too, didn't you?"

Susan nodded, not trusting herself to speak.

"It's a pity you left the ward when you did," said Daphne sympathetically. "Still, perhaps he'll write."

"It doesn't matter," Susan said, trying to sound as if she meant it.

But as the days wore on and no letter came, she began to realise that it was all over. In spite of her efforts to be sensible, depression took hold of her. Her work, which had never tired her young strength and enthusiasm until now, seemed all at once to overwhelm her.

Sister Martin told her to take a week's leave, and there was no arguing.

HER parents were so overjoyed to see her that she felt guilty for her reluctance to come home. Poor darlings, it was obvious that they missed her a great deal, though they tactfully said nothing about it.

"I suppose they sent you packing because you were poisoning the patients!" her father teased. "Never mind, we're used to it."

"Gracious, child, you're looking a bit peaky!" exclaimed her mother anxiously. "You must have a good rest while you're here — I suppose you're run off your feet in that hospital."

So every day she sat sunning herself in the garden, where the borders still made a blaze of colour. She often sat alone, as her mother had taken on some war work which kept her busy for much of the time. Susan's friends were all scattered, now, too; some in the Forces, some in other work of national importance. No-one sat idly at home nowadays, except a young nurse who'd been foolish enough to fall in love.

The doorbell rang when she was sitting in the garden one fine afternoon. She went reluctantly to answer it, then stood staring at the visitor, unable to believe her eyes. It was Richard.

He smiled diffidently, looking unsure of his welcome. "Hello, Susan."

A hundred thoughts raced through her mind, but only one surfaced. "How — how on earth did you find me?"

"I inquired at the hospital. Sister Martin gave me your address."

"Sister Martin!"

He nodded. "Yes, the old Battle-Axe herself. She's not so bad, actually — I wish I'd realised it sooner." He paused. "I hope I'm not interrupting anything, calling on the hop like this. It's not inconvenient, is it?"

"Oh, no," she replied, scarcely knowing what she was saying, "I wasn't doing anything special — just reading." She hesitated. "Would you like to come in for a minute, or are you on your way somewhere else?"

The moment she'd spoken the words, she could have bitten off her tongue in exasperation, realising how unwelcoming they sounded. The shock of seeing him unexpectedly like this had shattered her poise for the moment.

"Well, thank you." He moved promptly into the hall. "That's if you're sure I shan't be in the way?"

She took him through to the sitting-room and offered him some tea. The homely business of making and serving this helped to thaw the ice a little for them both, and soon they were chatting away together in their old style, though without any personal touches.

Suddenly, he leaned over and took her hand. "Susan — I had to see you again."

"Did you?" Her voice was not quite steady. "But you went off without even saying goodbye."

"I know — it was hell, believe me, Sue. But I only had a few hours' notice of my discharge, and there were fusses over transport, phone calls to my family and Lord knows what else. Besides, it seemed a better idea to write to you."

Night Scene

THE country scene lay softly
   silver-shadowed
Beneath the calm, ethereal full moon,
That peeped and peered through
   ragged whispy clouds,
Which tangoed swiftly to the
   wind's wild tune.

Gnarled, old trees were gowned in
   night's black velvet,
Shimmering ripples dressed the
   orchard pond,
A stealthy fox was clad in pewter tones
As he paused beneath a fern's bright
   frond.

The farmhouse slept in the trees'
   dark shadows,
Its windows reflecting the moon's
   cold light;
A cat's eyes glittered and his sleek
   fur shone
As a barn owl passed in swift,
   silent flight.

— *Gillian Riddle.*

"But you didn't," she said accusingly.

He shook his head. "I tried to, every day. The war effort must have been seriously impaired by the sheets of paper I got through, but it wasn't any good. I just couldn't get anything down in writing. I tore the darned things up, and decided the only possible thing was to see you and tell you myself."

He paused like a swimmer preparing for a dive. "Sue — marry me."

She caught her breath. Of course, she must be dreaming — she'd fallen asleep in the garden, and presently she'd wake to find all this was fantasy.

"Well, you needn't look so surprised, darling. You must have guessed how I felt about you, even though I never got a chance to do myself justice in that confounded hospital. Susan —" he leaned forward and gathered her in his arms — "Sue, for goodness' sake, answer me — please —"

S HE came to with a little start, and half-heartedly tried to push him away. "But, Richard, I can't — oh, it's crazy! We've only known each other less than three weeks altogether — it's such a little time —"

"Three weeks or three years, what's the difference? You're the one for me, Sue." He looked at her anxiously. "How about you?"

"I — I don't know." She tried to forget his nearness and think sensibly, but she found it impossible. "There's the war, and . . . and, oh, people just don't get married like this! They go around together for some time first, and then get engaged."

He released her for a moment. "That was fine in the old days before the war, but now everything's changed — don't you see? Now it's important to know what you want and grab it quickly before it vanishes for ever. There's only one thing really matters, darling — do you love me?"

She looked into his eyes and knew there could be only one answer. "Yes, Richard — oh, yes, I do!"

It was left to her parents, later on, to repeat her first startled objections.

"Better to wait a bit," her father advised. "See what the future brings."

"There's no future, sir, only the present," Richard replied quietly. "I'm rejoining my squadron in a fortnight's time."

Susan knew then that her mind was made up. "He's right, Daddy," she said firmly. "I don't want to wait."

They had a quiet wedding, and spent their brief honeymoon at a small country inn on the Thames. And all the time the leaves were turning from green to gold, russet or brown, then falling to the ground.

On the night before they had to return, he to his squadron, Susan to the hospital, they sat at the window of their bedroom watching the dusk gather about the peaceful countryside. A big yellow moon was swinging into view behind the tops of the trees on the darkening horizon. Somewhere an owl hooted.

"It's over," Susan said, with a break in her voice. "I wonder how long it will be before we're together again like this?"

"Perhaps not long," he said cheerfully, then held her close. "Remember this, darling — wherever I am, you'll know I'm close to you in my thoughts, always."

They returned to Susan's home next day, and she saw him off from the station. As she walked back again up a lane lined with chestnuts, she noticed a few conkers were still lying on the ground, evidently missed by the marauding hands of the local boys. She thought of what Richard had said that day in the hospital grounds.

A link between past, present and future — a kind of continuity . . .

A few days later, enemy aircraft crossed the coast near Dover and were quickly intercepted by squadrons of Hurricanes. Before long, the combatants had scattered over fifty miles of coastline and fierce dogfights were in progress. In one of the Hurricanes a young, fair-haired pilot gave a good account of himself before he was shot down. He died before the plane reached the ground. There was a new wedding ring on his finger, and the picture of a young, dark-haired nurse next to his heart.

It was Sister Martin who broke the news to Susan.

"Go home for a while," she said gently. "But not for too long. In the end, it's your work that will help you most. I know, my dear. I lost my fiancé in the First World War. You were wiser than I was — you took your chance of happiness."

SUSAN BRENT stirred, coming back from a long distance. She looked at her watch. In less than five minutes she'd be there.

She thought of the letter, and took it out of her handbag to pore over it for the umpteenth time.

It was written on somewhat crumpled Toytown notepaper with the uneven lettering and unconventional spelling of a six-year-old-child. A tender smile touched the woman's mouth as she pictured the little fair head bent over the paper, the tip of a small tongue protruding with the difficulty of the task.

Dear Gran,

I hop you will come to my house I love you a lot plees come to my house.

Love from Laura and Andy and Helen.

The rest of the page was covered in large sprawling crosses, with a more dignified line bearing the signatures of the two older children.

Susan's eyes were moist as she carefully replaced the letter in her bag and gathered the rest of her things together. As the train slid into the station, she gazed out of the window. Yes, there they all were, waiting to welcome her. Her son Richard, so like his father, his wife Kathie, with her warm smile, and three fair-haired children, the youngest dancing up and down with excitement.

She flashed a smile at the young airman as she left the compartment. Once she'd been told there was no future in loving Richard Brent, and in those first bitter months after his death, she'd believed it.

But now she knew better. Now she knew that his love reached out to her still through the priceless legacy he had left her — the son and the grandchildren whom he had never lived to see.

Yes, she thought with a grateful heart, there is always a future in loving. □

Y OU look a bit poorly this morning, Miss Simms," Ross Strachan told his secretary as she brought in his coffee.

"I think I'm sickening for something, Mr Strachan." She sniffed. "There's always some virus or other that gets a hold of a big building like this."

Ross nodded. "Quite."

"Will there be anything else, Mr Strachan?" Miss Simms paused to dab at her red-rimmed eyes.

Ross looked dolefully at his desk. It looked as though everyone in the city had been out collecting after a paper chase.

He looked up and smiled. "No, no. Just be sure you take care of yourself."

Alone, Ross sighed. Monday morning wasn't exactly his favourite. Especially here in this northern city he'd recently been "promoted" to. The crumbling old building didn't help either. It belonged in a Dickens novel.

Ross thought nostalgically of London, then frowned as he remem-

**by
MOIRA
WEBSTER**

bered the last girl in his life — a typical London jet-set type, out to enjoy herself on his money. At least here he was free from all that.

He stood up. It was time for Fred to call.

Ross crossed to the window and threw up the sash. Bright May sunshine greeted him across the city, throwing into relief the pocket handkerchief of a park far below his top-floor window.

"Come on, Fred," he called. "You're usually pecking at my window by now."

In response came the familiar whirring of wings, and Fred landed with a slight skid on the window ledge.

"Hi, there!" Ross greeted the big, slate-grey pigeon with the crimson feet. "Boy, am I glad to see you."

Fred waited patiently while Ross fished out his elevenses bag.

Fred cocked his head, apparently examining the day's menu. Greedily he began pecking at the biscuit crumbs, and Ross munched in unison.

"You know, Fred, if it wasn't for you I'd go clean off my trolley."

Fred nodded, then went back to his meal.

"We men must stick together. Life without women is nice and uncomplicated."

Fred cooed in agreement and Ross, elbows across the sill, enjoyed the close companionship he'd developed with this kindred spirit.

Fred was always alone, so he was obviously a bachelor pigeon who had his priorities right.

Fred finished gobbling and surveyed Ross with a bright, beady eye.

"Right then, mate, back to work," Ross announced reluctantly.

Fred fluffed out his feathers and, with a farewell nod, dropped off the ledge.

"And don't talk to any strange females!" Ross yelled after the plummeting, overweight bird. He was always amazed when Fred took wing, him being so fat. Considerably cheered up, Ross set about his work.

A PIGEON CALLED FRED

The People's Friend Annual

BY lunchtime he felt pretty smug about the way he'd got through it all. When Miss Simms brought him his usual two sandwiches from the canteen, Ross went over to the window and waited expectantly.

Ten minutes later he was still waiting. What on earth had happened to Fred? He never missed lunch. Maybe he'd flown headlong into high-tension cables or fallen under a bus or something.

Ross was actually wondering whether to phone the RSPCA casualty department when a sound made him freeze at the window. Staring down into the little park below, he saw where the commotion was coming from. Sitting demurely on a park bench was a young woman, surrounded by pigeons. All kinds of pigeons — and beaming in on her, a big fat one that looked remarkably like Fred . . .

Ross knew for sure it was Fred by the way the great feathered twit landed, feet splayed out as air brakes, terrified he was going to miss something.

Ross watched as Fred waddled towards the girl's outstretched hand and started pecking away happily. Ross sat heavily on his chair. His mate, his *only* mate, had deserted him. He didn't feel like his sandwich any more . . .

Suddenly, he stood up again. No use sitting here moping about it, he told himself. Get down there and have a closer look . . . He stuffed the sandwich into his pocket and went downstairs.

For a while Ross wandered about, then walked over towards the girl on the bench. No doubt about it — Fred had definitely turned traitor. He was guzzling away for all he was worth.

With a sigh, Ross walked on past them, towards the park gates. It was then that he heard the woman speak.

"There you are, Bessy, there's a good girl. I bet you haven't had a proper meal since you flew the nest."

Ross stopped abruptly, and before he knew it he'd turned to face her. "*Bessy*, did you say? Did you refer to that pigeon as Bessy?"

Startled, the girl looked up. "Why yes . . . as a matter of fact I did. She's nice, isn't she?" The girl smiled sweetly at him.

"But his name's Fred — and he's mine! I've been looking after him!"

"Fred?" She studied Ross, then the pigeon, and burst out laughing. "Fred . . .?" She put a hand over her mouth. "You can't call a pigeon Fred!"

Ross summoned up all his dignity. "I assure you, miss, that Fred is his name. And it's certainly not so improbable as *Bessy!*"

The girl's expression changed. "Improbable, you say?"

"Impossible, in fact! That pigeon is a bachelor!"

The girl shot Fred a questioning glance. He was looking up towards the top of a building as if he was considering flying up there to digest his lunch.

"Fred!" the girl said clearly.

Fred kept staring away from them.

"Bessy," the girl tried. Fred's head jerked round to look at her,

30

and he began waddling back into pecking distance.

"There you are," the girl said in triumph. "You see?"

"Rubbish," Ross protested. "With a handful of peanuts you could get any bird to answer to *any* name."

"They're not peanuts," she said shortly. "This is an approved diet for birds."

Ross glared at the box of bird food she held up for his inspection.

"And besides," she went on, "this poor pigeon is grossly overweight. Goodness knows what he's been eating recently. I've caught him — *her* — in the nick of time."

Ross felt the irritation building up in him. "Look, miss, all I want is Fred back. So if you'd kindly stop blackmailing my bird — "

"*Your* bird? You own her?"

"Well, er — not exactly . . ."

"She isn't your pet?"

"No, *he* isn't. But I've sort of adopted her — *him.*"

"You have adoption papers, Mr . . ."

"Strachan — and of course I haven't! I know a confirmed bachelor when I see one!"

Ross noticed a little ironic smile had come to her lips.

"You're an authority on bachelors I take it, Mr Strachan."

"Naturally. I'm one myself."

"Yes," she said. "Maybe you do have something in common. You don't look as if you're starving either."

Ross should have turned and walked away right then, but instead, to his horror, he found himself babbling out, "And if you were in digs with a landlady who cooks like mine does, I'll bet you'd be bell shaped yourself instead of . . . of . . ."

He gave her slim figure a rapid examination. Long, slinky legs, which he liked . . .

"Well, sort of skinny," he concluded.

He noted with grim satisfaction that the colour had come to her cheeks.

"I see . . ." Coolly brushing her hands free of bird food, she uncrossed her legs, smoothed her dress and stood up. Wings whirred, the girl's eyes flashed, and she walked away with her box of bird food, giving Ross a curt, dismissing nod.

A LONE, he sat thinking murderous thoughts about that woman, then Fred came winging back across the park. Air brakes on, he came to rest just outside assaulting distance of Ross.

"Well, a great help you were," Ross growled. "I thought we were mates — but what do you do? You go and suck up to some bewitching female and sell me out for a handful of bird food!"

Pigeons whirred above them, and Fred decided to join his own kind. With a stutter of feet he lolloped into the air and flew out of sight behind the neighbouring church. Ross returned to his work in a grey mood.

His pre-lunch enthusiasm had evaporated. He made heavy weather of his "in" tray for the rest of the afternoon, and Miss Simms was little help. Her eyes were getting redder, her sniff more regular by the minute.

Only the daunting prospect of his landlady prevented Ross from taking the rest of the afternoon off and going back to his digs, away from all the work.

He kept thinking of Fred, who'd taken the brunt of his irritation. No good turning on my own sex, he reflected regretfully. I'll have to make it up to him.

But even more he kept thinking of an independent, self-assured girl with long, slinky legs . . .

Eventually he let Miss Simms go home early, and decided he might as well do the same. As he was preparing to leave the building he remembered the uneaten sandwich in his jacket pocket.

He took it out and grunted at it. "Serves you right, Fred, if you're going to fall for this health food rubbish. Saved in the nick of time, indeed! Who does she think she is?"

He was halfway across the car park before a funny feeling came over him. He had planned to keep the sandwich until tomorrow for Fred's elevenses. Instead, passing a litter bin, he dropped the sandwich into it, then drove his car to a pet shop in town.

"What brand of bird food would you like, sir?" the proprietor asked him.

"Well, it's sort of blue and yellow with a bird table on it . . ."

"That will be the box you're talking about, sir," the man said testily. "You mean this one?"

Ross eagerly snatched it from him. "That's the one. The very one. I'll have half a dozen boxes."

"Half a dozen, sir . . ." The proprietor forced a smile, and wrapped up the six boxes, one eye on the street, as if he expected Ross to go berserk.

As he rang up the money in the till he remarked: "For an aviary, sir? I mean, that's a lot of bird food."

"Well, no, not exactly," Ross stammered. "Actually it's for Fred — that's a pigeon I know . . ."

"Fred . . . Of course," the man said, promptly locking the door behind the departing Ross . . .

★   ★   ★   ★

The evening meal was plain and stodgy — as usual. Ross felt like breaking open a box of bird food.

"Everything all right, Mr Strachan?" his landlady asked.

"Everything's fine," Ross lied, the way he did every evening. He went to the cinema wishing she would stick to sandwiches or salads or something equally easily digested.

Coming out of the cinema, he saw the girl. She was twenty people ahead of him, and he was hemmed in by outgoing cinema-goers.

He lifted a hand.

"Hey . . . Miss — er . . ."

Song Of The Lark

I LOVE to hear the wee lark sing
   His song at break of day,
When he rises from the dew-wet grass
To greet the month of May.

Spiralling to the heavens,
Warbling sweet and clear,
Each joyous trill,
Makes my heart thrill,
To the song I love to hear.

Gazing ever upward,
Keeping him in view,
Pouring forth such sweetness,
From a sky of cloudless blue,

Listening to his angelic song,
Fill the morning air,
Makes my heart soar with him,
Humbling all my care.
— *Katherine MacIntyre.*

Most people turned to stare at him. Except for her. When he got outside she'd disappeared.

"You twit!" he hissed at himself. "You don't want to speak to *her* anyway . . . !"

But it infuriated him to think that during that brief confrontation in the park she'd found out several things about him, whereas he didn't even know her name . . .

WHERE'S Miss Simms?" he asked the office junior just after nine o'clock next morning.

"She won't be in today, Mr Strachan," the girl told him. "Her mother just rang in to say she's gone down with some virus."

Ross stared at his workload. It took twenty minutes for personnel to organise a girl from the typing pool to act as his temporary secretary. Ross was half buried in paper when he heard the firm knock on his door.

"Come in!" he bawled, eyes down. He heard the door opening, then closing, and the faint rustling of a woman moving across to his desk. Then there was silence.

But there was something else . . . perfume — a familiar perfume . . .

Ross's head shot up. Oh no! It was her . . . !

"Good morning, Mr Strachan. Shall I sit down?"

Ross was still goggling. "The pigeon poisoner!" he said eventually.

She certainly didn't seem embarrassed about it, Ross thought grimly.

"Shall we start on the letters, Mr Strachan? You seem to be snowed under."

Ross's thoughts were turning cartwheels. In similiar situations in the past he'd always been masterful, calm . . .

"Er . . . yes, of course."

Halfway through the first letter he pushed his chair out from his desk. "Have you seen a film called, 'The Reckless Heart'?" he asked suddenly.

Her eyebrows lifted. "Not since last night, Mr Strachan. Why?"

"I just wondered, Miss . . ." He glanced at the name on his file . . . "Miss Tolchard."

They carried on for ten minutes more, but Ross's mind just wasn't on his work. "I see it says 'P. Tolchard' on this file. What does the 'P' stand for?"

"Paula," she answered.

"Nice name," he said, with a watery grin.

Paula Tolchard had her pen hovering over her shorthand pad, but Ross was finding it more and more difficult to concentrate.

"You're the last person in the world I expected to see in my office, Miss Tolchard," he said finally. "I suppose you're new here?"

"Relatively."

Ross went to rest his chin on his elbow on the desk edge. It never failed to impress people, except that his elbow slipped off. Paula

Tolchard kept her eyes on her shorthand pad.

"You, er . . . I assume you take your lunch in the park occasionally, Miss Tolchard?"

"Occasionally, Mr Strachan. How about you?"

"Me? Certainly not. Well, I sometimes take a quick stroll there to clear my head, that's all."

"Yes," she said. "I noticed."

"There's a lot of it about, you know, Miss Tolchard."

"A lot of what?"

"This virus thing. Miss Simms has gone down with it . . ."

"Quite."

There was silence for a full thirty seconds before Ross cleared his throat. "Yes, well, we'd better get on with this," he suggested.

As the time approached elevenses, Ross's attention kept straying to the window. Paula Tolchard followed his glance, and Ross saw her smiling to herself.

Any moment he expected the tap-tap on the window pane. Let Fred be on time today, he willed. Don't let the great chump let me down again . . .

"Anything wrong, Mr Strachan? Is it too stuffy in here for you? Shall I open that window . . . ?"

"No, no, everything's fine." She knows, Ross thought. She's making me feel just like my landlady makes me feel. Blasted women! Where's that pigeon gone?

"Are you sure you don't want me to open the window, Mr Strachan? You look a bit flushed."

"I'm perfectly all right, Miss Tolchard."

Ross looked in the opposite direction to distract her interest. He found himself staring at a pile of bird food boxes on the far table. She was watching them, too, and Ross could see she was struggling not to laugh. He felt the colour flooding into his own cheeks.

"If you don't mind, Miss Tolchard, I take my coffee at this time."

H E watched her leave the room, then shot over to the window, eyes raking the vicinity for Fred. Suddenly he heard a sound behind him. Paula Tolchard was at his desk holding his coffee.

"That was quick, Miss Tolchard. I was just having a breather. Gets a bit musty in these old buildings, you know."

"Perhaps it's all the paperwork," she suggested mildly.

Ross took his biscuits and stayed by the window, whistling casually. Without Fred to share his biscuits he felt stranded. Where was that bird? Suddenly he could stand the tension no longer. His head shot round.

"What was the idea of waylaying Fred yesterday, Miss Tolchard?" he demanded.

Her eyes flashed. "I didn't waylay her. She came to me of her own free will."

"*He* is easily led," Ross snorted.

"Relieved to have a decent diet, more like, Mr Strachan."

Exasperated, Ross stared out of the window. If Fred came now he would wring his neck.

"She doesn't appear to be coming today, Mr Strachan."

"What do you mean?"

Paula glanced at the six boxes of bird food. "I don't imagine that bird larder is for you, however bad your landlady's cooking may be."

Ross scowled.

"By the way, have you seen the film, 'The Reckless Heart'?" she asked.

"Me? Why, yes. As a matter of fact . . ."

"Did you like it?"

"No."

"Why not?"

"Well, the two main characters, they kept going on at each other too much . . ."

"Well, they were man and wife," she pointed out.

"Yes," he agreed.

He finished his coffee, and took the cup out to the trolley himself.

She was at the window looking out over the park when he returned.

"Looking for a pigeon to ambush?" he asked wryly.

"As a matter of fact I'm looking for Bessy."

"Bessy!"

"It may interest you to know, Mr Strachan, that I'm concerned about her."

"You ought to be. You nearly poisoned her — him — yesterday."

"Well, aren't you worried?"

"Of course I'm worried — I've looked after that pigeon for ages . . ."

B UT Fred didn't show up, and it was a very worried Ross who made his way home that evening. "It's all that woman's fault," he told himself. "Ever since she started interfering, the poor bird doesn't know what's happening . . ."

The next morning at elevenses time, Ross was back in his place by the window. There was still no sign of Fred.

"Where can she be?" Paula Tolchard said as she joined him.

"You've probably driven him away for good, Miss Tolchard," Ross answered sharply. "He was quite happy with all his biscuits and sandwiches till you turned up."

"Ladies don't like biscuits and sandwiches every day, Mr Strachan!" Her eyes were blazing again, Ross noticed. She went back to her shorthand pad and there was a few minutes of silence.

"Oughtn't we to settle this once and for all, Mr Strachan?" she said at last.

"How? By getting a pigeon expert to tell us Fred's gender?"

"Bessy," she insisted.

"Fred!" he shouted.

Deadlock. After staring each other out, Ross said, "All right, I'll admit I am getting a bit concerned. He's never been away this long before."

Paula Tolchard frowned. "Well, you can't be all hard man. You did see sense enough to change to approved bird food."

Fireworks went off inside Ross's head. But his anxiety for Fred overpowered his vexation with this girl. He crossed to the window and looked out.

Where is that dratted bird, he thought miserably.

For the next couple of days nothing changed. Miss Paula Tolchard continued to get on his nerves, and Fred the pigeon continued to remain invisible.

Ross's lunch hours and elevenses were torture without another freedom-loving bachelor to talk things over with. This particular lunch hour was worse than most, however — Paula had decided to stay in the office.

"No sign of him yet?" she asked, delicately sipping a fruit juice.

Ross bit back a sarcastic retort. She was worried about Fred as well, even though she did think he was one of her fellow liberationists.

"No," he said dejectedly. "What on earth could have happened to him?" Suddenly he reached a decision. "I'm going to look for him. Right now."

On The Lake

THE lakeland islands lift their trees
  Towards the blue of sky,
The water rippling round their shores
  Takes colour from on high.

Small boats weave in and out amongst
  The isles that dot the lake,
Like floating, coloured dragonflies,
  Leaving crystal spray as wake.

The guardian trees cast welcome shade
  As growing from green banks;
On summer days I sit and dream
  And give their maker thanks.
        — *Margaret Comer.*

Paula was on her feet in a flash. "Then I'm coming too," she announced.

They went downstairs in the lift, Ross frowning, Paula tapping one foot. They didn't speak again until they were in the park.

"How do you go about finding a lost pigeon?" she asked him.

"Easy," he said. "You find out where he lives, then see if he's at home."

Paula stared up at the parapets, all pigeon inhabited. "You're not going up there?" she asked dryly.

"If I have to."

Intently they both scanned the crowded parapets around the park. Pigeons of every shape, dimension and temperament — but no Fred.

"Where else would pigeons live, Mr Strachan?"

He was in the middle of shrugging his shoulders when the parish church clock chimed. Promptly one solitary pigeon rose in the air and wheeled above the bell tower.

"Fred!"

"Bessy!"

The both broke into a sprint towards the church, which stood two blocks behind the park. Ross arrived at the church porch panting heavily.

Paula was breathless too. "Inside?" she asked.

The small church was gloomy and empty. Ross pulled back a heavy drape and found the door leading to the bell tower. They clattered up the worn stone spiral steps, and Ross yanked back the bell tower door. Paula squeezed in in front of him, and as he followed her in, he heard a wonderfully familiar sound.

FRED, shadowy and unmistakable, whirred above them.

"Well, I've heard of bats in the belfry . . ." Paula began.

And there in the bell tower, the mystery was solved.

"Good grief!" Ross exclaimed.

"I don't believe it!" Paula gasped.

"I was wrong," Ross conceded.

"So was I," Paula said.

"Fred, you old scoundrel! You're no bachelor at all!"

"And you're certainly no lady," Paula added.

Fred, proud as a peacock — sorry, father pigeon — settled on a rafter, watching over his brood of newly-hatched baby pigeons.

"You're a family man after all," Ross said, shaking his head. "Now I know what you've been trying to tell me."

"Well, it certainly suits him." Paula sighed. "Although I don't suppose you'll be seeing so much of him for a while."

They watched as Fred strutted about, obviously very happy in his rôle as a new dad.

"Maybe there's more to this happy family business than I thought," Ross murmured. "There's one bachelor that seems to think so anyway . . ."

He turned to look at Paula, and was amazed to see she was blushing — and she wasn't even angry . . .

"Whatever shall I do with six boxes of bird food, Miss . . . Paula?"

"Feed Fred's family, of course — Ross."

Ross stared, grinned, then chuckled. "Excuse me, Fred. I've some settling up to do."

"Settling up?" Paula asked as he guided her down the bell tower steps.

"I think you and I should start again, Paula. We seem to have got our pigeons crossed."

Her eyes flashed. "What do you suggest then?"

"How about a slap-up dinner?" he said. She paused so dramatically that his eyes began to cloud in alarm. But then she laughed.

"All right," she said. "When it comes to correct diet, I can't bear to see anyone suffer — pigeon or man!" □

The Everlasting Echo

GERTRUDE LAMB was lonely but as usual she was fighting against it. And as always, or almost always, she was winning. The way to fight, she'd discovered, was to work as hard as you knew how and to rush furiously from place to place. Tonight she was typing the leaflets for the Church Jumble Sale.

The White Elephant Stall; The Good As New Stall; Refreshments . . .

She went faster and faster and made more and more mistakes. Gertrude wasn't an expert typist. She'd taught herself when she went on so many committees. She sighed as "white" ran into "elephant" and a half appeared instead of a full stop.

by MARGARET FOX

Outside the flat it was very quiet and her typewriter sounded unnaturally loud. Mrs Edmond's footsteps sounded on the stairs — she'd be going to see if her daughter had started her baby yet — and died away.

Soon she'd hear the rector's car and then she'd make some coffee . . .

Millie Hunter's great wedge-shaped shoes clattered past Gertrude's door. She'd be going to meet her boyfriend on the bridge. A pretty girl, Millie . . .

She, Gertrude, had never been pretty. Not even at Millie's age.

The village band would play selections from the "Yeomen Of The Guard," "Iolanthe" and the "Mikado," she typed furiously. Then she noticed she'd spelt "Iolanthe" wrong and angrily pulled the paper out of the machine.

Deciding not to wait for the rector's car, Gertrude went into the kitchen to make her coffee.

Just as she was switching on the kettle, she heard somebody at the door.

Gertrude marched confidently along the tiny strip of hall. She was sure her visitor would be either Mary from the newsagent's shop worrying about that bad debt, or the rector wanting advice about the special Women's Service. Either way she — Gertrude — was wanted.

Didn't they say in the village that they really didn't know what they would do without her? Sometimes she could almost believe it was true.

SHE switched on the hall light and opened the door. But it wasn't either the rector or Mary. It was a man she didn't recognise.

He was elderly and distinguished; she would surely have noticed him if he lived in the Dale. Gertrude was wary of strangers; she told herself she must be careful.

"Yes?" she said interrogatively but very coldly.

"Miss Lamb?" the man said. "Miss Gertrude Lamb?"

"Yes, but I'm afraid . . ." She moved forward to block the door. She wanted, too, to hide the early Staffordshire jugs on the sideboard. If he saw those . . .

"You wouldn't remember me," he said, "I couldn't expect you to. I'm Roger Oakley. We knew each other when we were young. Very young. Our family holidays in the Dale used to overlap."

"Oh, I . . . Of course I remember. How stupid. I . . ." Gertrude realised she was trembling. She couldn't go on.

Oh, she remembered all right. Of course she remembered.

Roger was five years older than she was. He'd been very handsome when he was a boy — as he still was.

When he had helped her across the stepping stones at the river she'd felt a queen. When he'd asked her to dance at the Saturday night Social, she cried herself to sleep because she couldn't follow his steps.

And when they'd both entered the wild flower competition she'd pretended she hadn't seen that Canterbury Bell down Lovers' Lane because she wanted him to find it and win . . .

I . . . I . . ." She began to stammer again. "Come in to the fire. It's chilly. I was just going to make some coffee."

She clutched at the idea of coffee as something solid in a heaving insubstantial world. Coffee was real. Tangible. She put the mug back in the cupboard and took out two of her Wedgwood cups. She emptied some sugar into a bowl.

"How . . ." They both spoke together when she went back into the sitting-room. Then they both laughed, self-consciously, like much younger, inexperienced people.

"I was going to ask how you were," he said.

"Quite well, thank you," she replied literally, then blushed and spilt some coffee in her saucer. "And I was going to ask how long it is since you were in the Dale."

"Forty years. At first it was exams and then after I qualified . . . Well, other things intervened.

"My wife was fond of travelling and we spent our holidays abroad. We had no children and when she died I went into a hotel. I'm still there."

"It must be difficult . . ." Gertrude began and then didn't know how to go on.

"And you?" he said at last. "What about you? You've told me nothing yet."

"There's very little to tell. When my parents died I was left alone. I decided to come here because I had such happy memories of our holidays. Now I feel I really belong, but of course, I'm terribly busy. Involved in everything. Committees . . ."

"I expect they couldn't get on without you."

"That's what they say." Gertrude smiled and tried to sound casual. "But you can't believe everything. I expect they're just trying to be kind."

"I'm sure they're not," Roger said gently.

She smiled and gave him some more coffee. It was what she wanted to hear.

"Do you remember," he said, "that picnic we had at Kisdon? There were some horses at the stile and you were frightened. I felt terribly grown-up and masculine when I chased them away."

"You were wearing a pink dress. Very pretty and bunchy. Not like the things they wear now, when you can't tell boys from girls."

Gertrude had never worn pink. It had always made her look terrible.

She wished he hadn't made that mistake.

But it was wonderful he had remembered the picnic. She'd never thought she would hear it mentioned again. She wouldn't tell him about the dress. It would only spoil things . . .

"I saw some horses at Kisdon last week," she said. "I still don't like them very much."

"Perhaps we could walk up there one day. I'm staying at River Farm for a week or two. We could go to the Falls as well. After all this rain they ought to be at their best.

"Do you remember that time we went after the flood and we had to come back over the fell because there was so much water in the valley? Everybody was out looking for us. I got in an awful row. I expect you did, too."

No, Gertrude hadn't got into a row. She hadn't ever been there. Roger and the boy from the post office had gone without her.

She'd lain in bed listening to the river thundering through the village and sucking some black things for her sore throat. She could still taste them, after forty-five years.

But Roger had forgotten that. Like the dress.

He was going on talking though. About the time when both families were there for Harvest Thanksgiving.

"We all went to the supper they had on the Monday evening. It was cold beef and apple pie and the Male Voice Choir gave a concert.

"I wanted to sit next to you but I couldn't. You were surrounded. I couldn't get near.

"So I sat behind and it went on awfully late because there were so many encores. Everybody pretended to be surprised when they got one but they all had an extra song on the piano waiting. Do they still celebrate the Harvest like that?"

Gertrude nodded but she couldn't speak. She had not been surrounded. She had never been surrounded in her life.

There had been an empty seat next to her until the interval. Then the farmer who rented them their rooms came and sat with her.

"What's this," he'd bellowed, "a grand young lass like you all on her own. What about putting up with an old joker like me for the rest of the evening, eh?"

She'd been hot with shame. Everybody had heard. Everybody looked at her. She'd been sure she'd never get over it. And for a long time she hadn't.

Roger had been sitting on the window ledge with the young people from the village. They'd clapped and shouted and sung all the choruses. Gertrude had thought how wonderful it must be to be like that and had been more jealous than she could bear.

SUDDENLY now she hated Roger. All these years she'd thought about him and idolised him and now when he had come back he was just making a fool of her. Mocking her for his own amusement.

He remembered nothing. Everything he'd said was wrong. Everything. Rubbish. The dress, the flood, the concert.

But why? What did it mean? What could he possibly want? Why had he come? It certainly wasn't money. She was sure of that.

She looked at him, she prayed to understand, and suddenly she knew.

He was lonely. Lonelier than he could endure.

Gertrude felt as though she was seeing him for the first time. He was afraid, too. Afraid of what she might say. Afraid of being found out. He was pleading with her.

And she loved him. She always had. If he could lie then so could she. After all, what was the difference between this and pretending about the Canterbury Bell all those years ago?

"Of course I remember," she said. "And it's just wonderful that you do, too. The dress, the flood. Oh, yes, I got into a row all right. And the concert is still just as packed and we still finish with 'Ilka Moor.' "

As she spoke, Gertrude saw his face change. Like a child's.

She was afraid they might become emotional and it was too soon for that yet so she began to gossip. About how the rector was a marvellous visitor, but a very poor preacher. About how the new doctor was let down by his wife and that the postmistress was failing and got into a muddle with licences.

Then she dug out an old picture album and he was entranced.

She suggested that tomorrow they go to Kisdon like he'd said. She'd make a very early lunch and then they would set off. Because she was sure the weather would be perfect. Absolutely sure.

When Roger had gone she finished her typing. This time when she spelt. "Iolanthe" wrong she only laughed. If they could find anybody else to do it better, let them. She didn't care.

But that night something happened. When Gertrude was wakened about half past one by the clip-clop of Millie's shoes she didn't want to cry as she sometimes did. Instead she just smiled and turned over and went to sleep again.

And it wasn't until they had been married for quite a long time that she acknowledged that, if she had answered Roger's need, he had just as surely answered hers. □

Gentle Spring

AH, spring, where have you been hiding?
You peeped from 'neath a crocus bud today.
Yet, if I told folk, they would not believe me,
"I was dreaming," they would say.

Yet I'm sure 'twas you I saw there
I could feel you in the air,
And each bud from young boughs growing
Seemed to show your tender care.

How glad I am that you are present,
Now I feel I want to live,
Long to see and feel your beauty,
Taste the pleasure that you give.

Now that winter has departed,
And you seem to want to stay,
I welcome you with open arms
Sweet herald of a lovely day!

— Jean Thomas.

THE diesel from the South slid silently into the platform. To Mattie, it felt unnerving, for she had never really got used to the changes in the city's railway system.

John had been a signalman in the old days, directing steam trains down the coast. He used to tell her that, from his high, glass box, he was master of all he surveyed — in charge of a complicated junction, switching points, waving to familiar faces as drivers passed on their way down the coast line.

She missed John terribly.

"Welcome to Glasgow Central," a cheerful voice boomed. Now there was another thing — the station itself. It was all so high-tech nowadays — electronic notice boards, destinations, times of arrival, even expected delays rippling into position by the touch of a button on some computer. All very impressive, Mattie had to admit.

She wished now that she had worn her best suit with the velvet collar. It would have been more in keeping with such grand surroundings, but because she was driving to the city and liked to feel comfortable at the wheel.

When her daughter phoned, Mattie imagined she heard resentment in Loraine's voice as she said, "I'm sorry it's been so long, Mother, but I think Bobby will explain."

Loraine hadn't changed much. She'd always been secretive and uncommunicative. Even when her father died she had been unable to contact Loraine for the funeral. It turned out it had something to do with her husband, Harvey, having to go abroad urgently and how, on the spur of the moment, she'd gone with him.

Yes, it had really been too bad, for Loraine had always remained the apple of her father's eye, and she believed the girl adored him.

MATTIE sighed. It had been the same story since Loraine left

SUMMER WITH BOBBY

home. One excuse after another why the family could not travel north. But now Mattie was waiting for Bobby, her one and only grandson. She felt her heart lift at the thought.

What would young Bobby look like after ten years? Mattie had gone with her husband to the child's christening in Oxford, and remembered a rather shrivelled little face, a babe who was for ever crying.

Loraine was her only daughter but they had never been close. John had always known how to deal with Loraine, how to jolly her out of dark moods.

Mattie had no patience with moodiness. If one said anything sharp to the girl she would not speak for days, isolating herself in her room with a book.

Then, Loraine had married Harvey Oliver. As different as chalk and cheese, they were . . . He was a hale fellow well met.

What if Bobby took after Loraine? It would be some summer if the pair of them had to watch every word.

Oh Lord! There he was . . . walking down the platform, ten years old and already over five feet tall. He was Loraine's boy and no mistake . . . same wide forehead and dark brown eyes, and polite as they come . . . holding out his hand in greeting.

"Gran?"

"It's yourself, Bobby."

He was holding a large bunch of flowers.

"These are from Mum."

They were very nice flowers and must have cost a packet, but Mattie could not have put a name to one bloom. Imported no doubt from some foreign country . . .

"How is your mum?" she asked quickly, and the boy looked at her with those frank brown eyes.

"As well as can be expected, I suppose."

Now that was a strange thing for a boy to say to his grandmother for a start? It was obvious Loraine had him well primed. That girl had always been on the defensive, too, Mattie remembered.

"Well, come along, Bobby. The car's over there."

by
AILIE
SCULLION

SHE did not intend sharpness to creep into her voice. Had she not made herself a promise when agreeing to the boy coming up for the summer? All the mistakes made in the past would be remedied now. She would become a friend to Loraine's boy, and if this succeeded, perhaps she could win back her daughter's affection?

"I'll carry my own case, Gran."

She had been stooping towards the handle when the voice stopped her.

"But you have a haversack and that thing over there . . ."

"It's an inflatable canoe.

"Oh, I know what it is right enough, Bobby, and there was no need to take it all the way up here. I have proper canoes in the garage. Now did you know that our house sits beside the water? The lawn sweeps right down to the beach and you can see out to the tail of the bank from our window."

"Mum told me."

The boy's voice was as deflating as the rubber canoe they now had to stuff in the boot. They reached the car, John's old battered saloon, and, leaning forward, Mattie opened the boot which took all the boy's luggage nicely. But the inflatable canoe refused to fit and to the boy's consternation had to be stowed in the back seat. She stifled a giggle and he looked at her suspiciously.

"What is it?" he enquired.

She felt foolish now. "I was just thinking how it would be if that plug came out as we were driving. Can't you see it, Bobby? I'd need to open the sunroof."

The young serious face turned towards her and reprimanded, "It has a safety catch."

Oh dear! He was Loraine's son, sure enough.

ONCE on the open road she put her foot down hard on the accelerator and could hear the quick intake of breath beside her. "It's all right, dear. I've never lost a passenger yet."

The boy remained silent for miles and Mattie's heart sank. They were not hitting it off. It was going to be history repeating itself.

"How's your dad?" she asked now, deciding to try for safer ground. After all, Mattie had nothing but admiration for her son-in-law. Harvey was an ambitious young fellow who could charm birds out of trees and had done so well for himself in business.

It was terrible how families grew apart. When Loraine married, Harvey whipped her off to London where he worked. At first, there were letters in her daughter's neat hand telling of Erik's many successes, about the new job that meant he required to move about such a lot and that was why they never had a proper home and why Bobby went to boarding school . . . an only son, she'd thought, and sending him off so young?

"I think he's well enough" the voice beside her spoke coolly. "We don't hear from him much."

The car swerved slightly and they did not speak again for some time.

"Didn't you realise he'd left us? That's why Mum suggested I might spend the summer with you. She thought it wouldn't be right for me to be in the flat all day when she was still at work."

★　　★　　★　　★

A wave of compassion swept through Mattie. And poor Loraine! She didn't deserve this.

She remembered, now, John's reservations about their son-in-law.

▶ *over*

FAMOUS WOMEN

MATA HARI (1876-1917).

This Dutch dancer, courtesan and spy, was known also by her real name — Margaret Gertrude Zelle. She was born at Leeuwarden in the Netherlands.

Married to Captain Campbell MacLeod, an officer of Scottish origin of the Dutch Colonial Army, she accompanied him to Java and there learned to practise ritual Oriental dances.

After divorcing her husband she sailed back to Europe, assumed the stage name of Mata Hari and danced with great success in several European capitals.

In 1908 she settled in Paris, where she made full use of her beauty as well as her personal charms and was well known in French political circles.

It was then that she began to act as a secret agent in Germany's pay. She went to Berlin a few days before the beginning of World War I but returned to Paris through the Netherlands in 1915.

As she was suspected by both British and French intelligence services, traps were set for her and she was eventually caught. Tried in July 1917 by a French court-martial, she was convicted of being a spy and sentenced to death.

Mattie could not find it in herself to quiz her grandson, but once this shattering piece of news had been absorbed there appeared to be a change in atmosphere. Bobby seemed almost relieved and began to study the changing scenery, the river where small yachts bobbed on anchor, a large grey-coloured ship nosing through the channel, its ominous looking radar twirling eerily.

"A Naval patrol boat, Gran?"

She nodded gloomily. "We'd better give it a wide berth when we go canoeing, eh?"

He looked at her now and for the first time she saw a twinkle in his brown eyes.

"We, Gran?"

"Why not? Your grandad and I learnt river canoeing at the outdoor centre. Wait until you see my draw strokes."

BOBBY loved the house which John had renovated for their retirement . . . an old cottage built more than a century ago and almost on the shore. Mattie remembered how John had painted it pink just the year before he died.

Whenever it was fine, the couple would take their meal out on to the lawn and picnic under a stripped umbrella, and Mattie used to swear the seagulls smelt the tea for they would perch in a long patient row along the seawall awaiting the crumbs.

The canoe lessons had been for her fiftieth birthday. John must have grown tired of listening to her rave on about how she would love to canoe, especially when a group of young people would paddle past their lawn. The outdoor centre instructor did not blink an eyelid when they booked in for lessons.

That was the beauty about living practically on the water. You could choose your moment . . . and today the surface was so smooth it felt as though it would mist over if you breathed upon it. There was a pink haze hanging over the peninsula towards which they were heading, and for a moment Mattie thought it resembled a tropical island.

Bobby paddled directly ahead of her, turning occasionally to make certain she was on course. He had assumed command easily and Mattie, for once, held her tongue.

In the weeks he'd been staying with her she had grown accustomed to Bobby's ways. Sometimes he seemed much older than his ten years, other times almost vulnerable, and he was so like Loraine it caused her heart to miss beats.

Perhaps with middle-age came maturity. John always insisted she would grow up some day. Perhaps if Loraine were here now they might become . . .

"Watch just ahead, Bobby . . . there's a nasty wee cross-current."

"Yes, I saw it, Gran."

Mattie bit her lip. She was improving, but there was still a long way to go. She was still "old bossy boots" whom John would chide jokingly in the old days, but then John had always known how to handle her impulsive outbursts, and invariably got his own way in the end.

She realised to her sorrow now that she had bossed her daughter ruthlessly. John had seemed content to puff on his pipe whilst she set her daughter straight, and would only later point out where she might have gone easier.

Mattie realised now that she had never really given Loraine a chance to prove herself.

THERE was not a breath of wind as they pulled their crafts ashore at Ardentinny. It had been a long trip but very satisfying, and as they found a suitable place to lounge, Mattie pulled out the rubber bag from the canoe and undid its pull-string, tossing Bobby an apple and packed sandwich for afterwards.

He was smiling at her and suddenly she realised the dark eyes were filled with . . . yes, admiration! She noticed the look earlier when she appeared in her wet suit . . . not bad either for a woman of sixty, but then Mattie noticed the boy's look was also tinged by apprehension.

"Mum was right about you, Gran. You are good at everything."

She was not sure if this was meant to be a compliment.

"She used to say she became an old buttery fingers whenever you were around, that her sponges collapsed and she dropped stitches when she knitted, but yours were always perfect."

Out of the mouths of babes and sucklings . . . Bobby's remark was not a compliment.

She was learning a great deal about herself since Bobby came to stay. Indeed, what she learnt did not make her feel very proud. A daughter, who had lived in awe of her, feeling all the time that she could not live up to her mother's great expectations.

It was incredible but true. Mattie Brown had always prided herself upon being outspoken and frank, but in her daughter's eyes she must have been overwhelming. Was this why Loraine married the first man who flattered her and implied she was wonderful.

But there was no subterfuge about Bobby. He had inherited his gran's frank approach right enough, and nor did he spare her when it came to home truths.

"I imagine there should be good fishing here." The same frank voice broke in on her thoughts now.

"Um" his gran agreed, "Mackerel by the shoal and cod, and if you are really in luck you can claim a salmon. Your grandad and I caught an eight pounder once. We could try the rods some night if you like."

"I'd like that."

Bobby came and sat close to her, his thin legs stretched out before him. She was about to embark upon another lecture . . . that it was high time she fed him up, put some flesh on those bones, then Mattie caught herself in time. She was beginning to realise the harsh effect her thoughtless lectures had upon others, yes, even the words about to be released now . . . implying that his mother did not feed him properly.

Thankfully, Bobby did not take after his gran totally with his own style of outspoken truths, but was blessed by an amalgam of genes. She recognised in him the straight-forwardness of her late husband John, and his knack of remaining silent when she went off with all guns firing. But she saw too a sensitivity that she now realised had been in Loraine.

"I suppose you can swim like a fish, too," he said in his matter-of-fact voice."

She nodded almost apologetically. "But I don't think I will, today, Bobby. I feel stiff after our long trip, but you go ahead, dear. You must remember that I'm sixty now."

"You could have fooled me, Gran."

She looked up suspiciously but his expression gave nothing away.

BOBBY decided he would not go swimming after all and seemed content to remain by her side. He was such a strange little boy — not at all what she had expected. During the long light evenings she imagined he would wish to go out and play in the garden, kick a ball about the grass, or complain that there were no children of his own age with whom to make friends. Instead, he seemed content to remain inside.

He would speak quite openly about his life at boarding school where he had been forced to take part in games when he would much rather have read a book; of his parents' recent divorce, which he himself had known was on the cards for years.

It was as the boy discussed this adult subject that Mattie began to feel wretched. Where had she been all these years when her girl needed her so?

It was through the boy that Mattie began to understand other features of the past; how it had never been her daughter's wish to send her only child away, but desperately hoping that by following her husband's hectic lifestyle, their shaky marriage might be saved, she'd agreed.

▶ over

CULZEAN CASTLE

CULZEAN CASTLE in Ayrshire, was created by Robert Adams in the 1780s for the Earl of Cassillis. It overlooks the lower Firth of Clyde. It is a beautiful building and thousands of visitors call each year.

The suite of rooms in the castle which used to be reserved for General Eisenhower as his Scottish residence are always of interest to sightseers.

The name "Culzean" is pronounced "Cul-ain" and refers to the caves over which the castle is built.

Mattie had never really cuddled her own daughter, after infancy, and had truly believed Loraine would not have encouraged her. But now Mattie would find her hand straying to the child's head, and Bobby, in turn, would draw close, leaning his head against her shoulder as they watched "Coronation Street" or argued over crossword puzzles.

★   ★   ★   ★

Mattie felt luxuriantly tired after a hot bath that night. The stiffness had left her bones and she thought she might watch the film on television — an old classic. She'd seen it many times before but they could have a fine discussion later. She told Bobby it was about a family who'd stuck together through thick and thin, facing one adversity after another.

"That should be a novelty," the boy remarked shortly, and Mattie felt the knife turn slowly.

"I'm sorry, Bobby. I never meant it to sound like that."

"I know, Gran. We all says things we don't mean."

They sat silently watching the film until the last strains of music disappeared, and leaning forward Mattie switched off the set.

"This is the night Mum said she would phone," a young voice reminded, and Mattie nodded, her teeth biting hard on her lower lip.

As if she could forget? Tonight she would hear Loraine's decision.

Bobby had been staying with her now for six weeks and she had loved every moment, but she knew the boy was missing his mother.

Last week there had been a long discussion on the phone and Mattie sensed her daughter's indecision, and knew the reason for this. The old wounds were still there and now she was thinking her mother was attempting to replace her love for Bobby, and appeared to be succeeding going by Bobby's animated descriptions of the adventures he was having with his "supergran."

Mattie, who hoped she was older and wiser now, attempted to sweeten the pill by inviting the girl to come north as soon as she was able.

"I need to work, Mother," Loraine pointed out, and Mattie had thought about this long and hard. Loraine was a qualified history teacher although she had not taught in years. Then, two weeks ago, Bobby had drawn her attention to an advert in the paper.

They sat side by side on the settee, Mattie with her knitting on her knee, Bobby with one eye on his half-finished jigsaw, the other on the phone.

"The old woman in the film was good, wasn't she, Gran? She seemed to hold the family together."

She nodded her head. Such wisdom from the mouth of a child.

The phone rang and the boy sat erect.

Mattie touched the child's crown as she pushed herself out of the settee.

"Hello, Loraine. Yes, dear, we are both fine. A lovely time, yes,

I'll let you speak to Bobby as soon as we are through. How did you . . . Oh, Loraine, I'm so glad . . . no honestly, lass, I couldn't be more pleased and I hear the headmaster is a fine man. Do you remember he taught you when you went to the academy?

"Yes, I'm sure you're making the right decision. We'll have a grand time together and Bobby loves it here. Yes, I'll let you speak to him directly, but first can I say something, Loraine? I'm so happy about how you've decided. It's like being given a second chance and believe me, love, I will not make the same mistakes twice. No . . . it's true, Loraine, I know now that I got it all wrong. You see I've learned such a lot about myself since Bobby came to stay. He's quite a lad."

SHE handed the receiver to her grandson and sat down again. Loraine had applied for a job at the local high school teaching history. It was after Mattie sent the cutting showing the employment advertisement — the one Bobby had pointed out to her.

Mattie could feel her heart thumping against her rib cage. It was not often one got a second chance to get to know a daughter. This time she was not going to make the same mistakes . . .

" 'Bye, Mum." The phone clicked into place and she watched Bobby, his long thin legs protruding from striped pyjamas as he crossed the room towards her, face creased into a rare smile.

"That's all right then, isn't it, Gran?"

He curled himself into a ball, his thin shoulder-bones showing through a blue dressing-gown.

"We will be a proper family again, won't we . . . like those folk in the film?"

She did not miss the longing in his voice, and leaning forward drew him towards her.

"Oh, Bobby, love, you can bet your life on it!" □

DURHAM TOWN

ONE of the most visually-exciting cities in Britain is Durham. The magnificent Norman Cathedral and the castle form a centre-piece and stand proudly on a sandstone bluff.

The old city of Durham was originally confined to the rocky peninsula that is almost enclosed within a loop of the Wear, and was dominated by its cathedral and castle. Today it is essentially unchanged.

In 1832 the university took over the castle but the superb twelfth-century buildings remain, scarcely changed in appearance. It is one of the grandest sights in the country. The best view is from eighteenth-century Prebend's Bridge.

A small town, Durham has its roots firmly in the past as it faces the future. ▶ *over*

HERE IS MY

HEART by LYNN BRETON

"B EDTIME, you two!" Deborah Barlow said to her young neice and nephew just as the telephone rang.

Her heart lurched. This time it *must* be Sandy Campbell.

But it was her sister, Clare, phoning from the hospital in France. Clare's voice was reassuring, giving one more banishing push to the small cloud of dread that had hovered since her first emergency call.

Deborah had been in her flat when Clare had phoned, telling her that her brother-in-law, Peter, had been badly injured in a car crash. He had been attending a legal conference in France and Clare wanted to fly over there immediately. Could Deborah be a dear, and look after the children?

Luckily Deborah had been able to get time off work and had taken the first train to Surrey.

"Oh, Clare, I'm glad," she said now, into the mouthpiece. "It's wonderful that Peter's making such a splendid recovery. Having you there beside him must have helped.

"Don't worry about a thing at this end. Of course I'm coping. The children are behaving perfectly. Well, let's just say they're doing their best."

In the narrow hall her neice and nephew jostled for a place by the telephone. Deborah grinned at them. "They're right here. I think they want to talk to you!"

Jane, hopping from one foot to the other, snatched at the receiver, but big brother, Robert, took it from her firmly. Between them, they took up the last seconds of Clare's call.

They were beaming at each other when they hung up, sharing the relief that the news had been good. How could she possibly mind that the call had not been from Sandy? Deborah asked herself.

"Bedtime now, Jane!" she insisted again.

"Can't I just finish my book?" Jane wailed.

"Books," pronounced twelve-year-old Robert, "will soon be obsolete as instruments of learning."

"I'm not *learning*, I'm just reading," Jane corrected him. "It's a happy-ever-after book."

Then she added, with barely a pause: "Aunt Deb, why haven't you ever got married?"

There might still be time." Deborah smiled at Jane.

"But you're getting on a bit, now, aren't you?" observed Robert. "A quarter of a century."

Ancient! Deborah thought ruefully. She glanced at her dark-haired, dark-eyed reflection in the mirror above the fireplace. She had not aged noticeably since that morning, but she had to admit to herself she looked her age. Twenty-five sounded much more youthful than a "quarter of a century."

"Yes," said Robert. "It's time you got married. I'd like to have another man in the family."

"Milk, Jane!" Deborah set a glass down beside her niece, and hoped Robert would drop the subject.

She could never hope to keep one jump ahead of Robert. He was such a serious boy. Son of a lawyer, grandson of a lawyer, it seemed he was all set to uphold the family tradition.

She thought again of Sandy Campbell, who had decided not to follow in his schoolmaster father's footsteps, but become a doctor instead.

By the time she got back to town, maybe Sandy would know the results of his finals.

After that, he would have to do a year as a house surgeon. That year, Deborah thought, would give her time to come to terms with the fact that he would disappear from her life to do general practice in the North of Scotland

She sometimes wondered whether she would ever have got beyond saying "Good morning" to Sandy Campbell if Kate Mitchell hadn't been her neighbour.

▶ *over*

CALEDONIAN CANAL

FAMOUS as an engineering feat in the early 1800s, the Caledonian Canal runs clean across Scotland from the Beauly Firth near Inverness to Loch Linnhe near Fort William.

It was built to avoid time and the hazards of sailing round the North of Scotland by the stormy Pentland Firth and Cape Wrath. The total length of the canal is over 60 miles — some 22 miles of which is constructed.

It is the longest "short-cut" in Britain, running in a straight diagonal through twenty-nine locks and three lochs — Lochy, Oich and Ness.

Pleasure craft and Nessie-seekers abound on the canal, and thousands of visitors touch a part of it every summer.

This illustration is of the canal at Fort Augustus.

CALEDONIAN CANAL at FORT AUGUSTUS : J CAMPBELL KERR

HER flat was just a room-and-a-half in a big Victorian house converted for the use of hospital staff. She had just got a job as dietician and the day she moved in she had met Kate on the landing.

"Hello! You must be Deborah Barlow — new tenant, first-floor front, I'm Kate Mitchell, first-floor back." Kate had dumped a bag of shopping on the floor and scrabbled for her key. "I'm dying for a coffee. Come in and join me, won't you?"

There were three flats on the first-floor landing and Deborah had wondered who lived in the third. Kate put her in the picture.

"Your other neighbour is Sandy Campbell, a medical student. But he's older than most of them. Which means he has to work that much harder. You could say — all work and no play . .

"No," Kate contradicted herself. "That's not fair. He's dedicated, that's all. He took a science degree and taught for a time but then he switched over to medicine."

Kate's look was thoughtful. "His father's a village schoolmaster somewhere in the wilds of Scotland. He was apparently opposed to the changeover but I've a hunch Sandy will make a good doctor if he lives to take his finals."

"Isn't he likely to live?" Deborah was dismayed.

"Sandy Campbell is clued up on blood vessels and arteries but he tends to overlook the fact that the human animal has to be fed. As a dietician, you'll know all about that."

Kate filled up their coffee cups.

"Apart from myself and Sandy Campbell, you'll not see much of the other occupants. Though you'll probably come up against Elaine Morgan who has the flat below yours. She's a perpetual borrower."

Elaine certainly was. She came up to borrow sugar just a day or two after Deborah had moved in.

"Expecting visitors?" Elaine asked, watching Deborah make the tea. She was a good-looking girl packed full of confidence. She also missed nothing.

"Only Kate. And maybe Sandy Campbell. Stay and join us if you like."

"Sorry — I'm going out. Thanks all the same." Elaine was filling a cup with sugar.

"In case you have ideas about Sandy, take a hint — forget them. He has a one-track mind — or two tracks, running together. To get through his finals and to stay emotionally uninvolved. Make one move towards him and he retreats a mile."

Kate, coming in as Elaine went out, said, "She should know. She tried hard enough. But she's moving soon, so good luck." She chuckled. "Don't mind me, I'm only being catty!"

At the same time, Deborah found herself remembering the warning, even after Elaine had moved.

Sandy Campbell was a long-limbed man with features that were a shade too craggy to be handsome, a thatch of brownish hair, an emphatic chin. His eyes were grey and, thought Deborah, wary. He also looked, as Kate had suggested, as if he never remembered to eat.

"Eating's important," Kate maintained, watching with interest as Deborah lifted a casserole from the oven. "But I'm afraid I'm not much of a cook. That smells marvellous."

"Be my guest!" Deborah grinned. "There's enough for two."

The shared casserole became a custom. It was more economical, Kate would insist, dumping meat and vegetables in Deborah's kitchen to cook for two. Or for three.

They soon began sharing their meal with Sandy Campbell whenever it was casserole day. Occasionally they ate in state, with a bottle of wine brought along by Sandy, but mostly one of them just carried the remains of the casserole into his room and dumped it among the clutter of medical textbooks. The dish always came back empty.

Deborah felt no nearer to knowing Sandy Campbell. He was pleasant but unforthcoming; polite but uncommunicative. Then she found Ferdinand.

She found the little bird at the foot of the steps that led up to the house; a pathetic bundle of feathers, with a rusty breast. She picked him up, carrying him in carefully-cupped hands. She met Sandy Campbell on the landing.

"It's a robin," she explained. "He's — alive, but I think he's hurt."

"Let me see," Sandy said.

She watched as Sandy examined the bird.

"I think he's been in a fight," he said at last, "and come off worst."

"Perhaps he's a pacifist." Deborah smiled.

"Like Ferdinand the bull in the cartoon?" Sandy added with a grin.

Deborah looked up, meeting the unexpectedly dancing grey of his eyes. He should relax and laugh more often, she thought, feeling one step nearer knowing Sandy Campbell.

B Y the next morning Ferdinand had perked up and took breakfast from Deborah's hand. Sandy came to see him and began to pop in every morning, just to see how he was.

By the end of the week Ferdinand was flying round the room. On Saturday he spotted an open window, and sailed through it before Deborah could stop him. He perched for a moment on the wrought iron balcony rail, then was gone.

Deborah missed him dreadfully. But not the way she would miss Sandy Campbell, she admitted to herself, if he ever flew out of her life.

The next day Kate came bouncing into Deborah's room.

"I'm driving down to the coast to see my aunt," she explained. "Come with me — Sandy's already said yes. It isn't often we're all free together — and it's a beautiful day! Take your swimming costume."

It *was* a beautiful day. Fresh and clear and warm. Kate dropped them by the beach and drove on to see her aunt.

They walked slowly along the beach, examined rock pools, threw pebbles at the waves. They ate the picnic lunch Deborah had brought, and drank the coffee Sandy bought from a kiosk along the beach. Then they lay in the sun on the dunes.

Sandy said softly, breaking the silence, "Tell me about yourself. I know your father's a vet, and that you've a sister and a brother or two, but nothing else. Fill in the background."

"My two older brothers are married, and farming," Deborah replied drowsily. "My younger brother is still at home." She closed her eyes against the glare of the sun. "Home's a very lived-in house, with mud on the drive."

"So you scraped the mud off your shoes and came up to the big city?" Was there a hint of wryness in Sandy's tone? Her eyes were still closed but Deborah no longer felt drowsy.

"I felt I wanted a change, if that's what you mean," Deborah replied, opening her eyes and blinking against the sun. Sandy was looking at her but she couldn't read his expression. "Just like you when you switched from teaching to medicine," she added.

Sandy nodded. "My parents weren't keen on the idea but Fergus Mackay, our village GP, was on my side. Even so, Mum and Dad still think of it as a gamble."

"No gamble," Deborah predicted. "You'll make it."

"Thanks for the vote of confidence!" Sandy grinned and kissed her.

IT was just a token kiss and he was obviously unaware of the havoc it played with Deborah's emotions; unaware that the earth seemed to tilt and the sun split up into a kaleidoscope of fragments.

"Fergus Mackay," Sandy went on, "isn't getting younger. He'll want somebody to take over when he retires."

"He wants it to be you?" Deborah asked vaguely.

"I owe him that," Sandy said. Then added the touch of dry humour. "It also happens I want to."

Before Deborah could reply Kate's shadow fell between them.

Deborah sat up, Sandy caught her hands, hoisting her to her feet.

"I promised my aunt I'd take you both back for tea." Kate explained. "She loves company and I left her baking scones and worrying in case they didn't turn out right."

The scones were featherlight. But Sandy would have eaten them, Deborah realised, had they been hard as granite. She was learning more and more about Sandy Campbell.

"My aunt," Kate remarked, when they were alone in Deborah's flat that night, "thinks you and Sandy are a lovely couple. And note that word couple. She only uses it about the betrothed."

Deborah said, dryly, "Bless her! And, Kate — thank you for today."

"It was a pleasure," Kate replied, "to have you and Sandy along. Don't underestimate yourself, Deborah, where's he's concerned."

"D EAR Kate!" Deborah breathed.

"I'm sorry, did you say something?" asked her nephew, Robert.

"Sorry, Rob I was thinking aloud." She laughed.

"Yes. It sometimes helps," declared Robert sagely. "I think I'll go up to bed. It could be fine tomorrow."

It was. But only just.

"Can I ride my bike in the drive?" demanded Jane when a watery sun struggled out between the gloomy clouds.

"Yes, I don't see why not," Deborah replied. "Rob, could you pop down to the grocer's for me?"

Robert agreed immediately and Deborah watched him walk sedately down the drive. The rain had stopped, but the trees still dripped and the drive gleamed damply.

The gleam was treacherous. Jane's cry brought Deborah rushing outside. The little girl was lying on the ground beside her overturned bicycle.

Pain and panic brought more screams from Jane. Deborah scooped her up and headed for the house, trying to calm her by talking soothingly.

Jane's screams had diminished to a whimper when

Ring Out The Old, Ring In The New

F AREWELL, farewell, to the passing year,
The bells are ringing loud and clear.
Come, listen to their gladsome song,
Ring in the right, ring out the wrong.

Then let us make our vows anew
In all we say and all we do,
Thus choosing now to do our best
Will make us work with greater zest.

Farewell, farewell, the sun has set,
The goals we made let's not forget.
The old year fades into the night,
The glorious dawn breaks clear and
    bright.

Awake, awake, with joyous smile,
We will attain that extra mile.
It's time to make our dreams come
    true,
Yes, this the hope for me and you.
— *Margory Green.*

Robert said, from the kitchen door, "I suppose she fell off her bike?" His calmness was comforting.

"Let me see," said Sandy Campbell, from somewhere behind Robert.

"Sandy!" Deborah brushed a wisp of hair from her eyes. How he had found her, she didn't know. What mattered was that he was here.

"I met your nephew along the road. I was looking for the house." Sandy's tone was pleasantly conversational. The dregs of panic — her own and Jane's — slid away.

Sandy's skilled fingers touched Jane's nose, and he grinned at her. 'Have you been having a fight with somebody?"

"A gatepost," Jane answered, importantly.

Sandy picked her up, carried her into the sitting-room, and set her down on the settee. "You lie there for a wee while, young woman," he said gently.

"Are you a doctor?" Jane asked brightly.

"Since yesterday," Sandy said.

"Sandy!" Deborah looked at him. She should have been saying the conventional things; murmuring congratulations. But somehow the words would not let themselves be spoken. "Sandy — "

"I wanted my girl to be the first to hear the news," Sandy said, quietly. "She wasn't around, so I bullied Kate into giving me this address."

"Why," demanded Robert, "did you have to bully Kate?"

"A good question." There was the humour in Sandy's eyes. "But this is a private conversation, Robert, between Deborah and me. We're going outside to finish it. Keep an eye on your sister, will you now?"

THERE was a scent of stone drying in the sun. Wet grass, damp air. The warmth of Sandy's hands. Sandy kissing her.

"Kate," Sandy said after a few minutes, "seemed to doubt the honour of my intentions."

"I," she said, "doubted whether you had *any* intentions."

Sandy held her close. "I had to get through my finals, darling. I wanted to have something to offer you. And there's another thing — " Sandy's grey eyes held doubt.

"What other thing?" Deborah prompted gently.

"I want to go back to Scotland. Could you stand the wilds?"

I would go anywhere with you, Deborah thought. The Arctic, Timbuktu . . . anywhere. She couldn't find the elusive words to tell him but Sandy seemed to get the message. He kissed her again.

When they looked round, Robert was watching them from the open french windows.

"I think," Sandy announced solemnly, "we should legalise our position."

"You mean you're going to marry Deborah?" Robert asked. "I'd rather hoped you would. I'd better tell Jane. I promised to keep her informed." He disappeared indoors again.

"Well, that seems to settle that," Sandy remarked.

Deborah nodded. Then said, feeling very humble, "Sandy, I've never been to Scotland."

"My folk," Sandy said, with perception, "have always wanted a daughter. And old Fergus Mackay will eat out of your hand."

"Like Ferdinand?"

"Well, almost." Sandy chuckled. "But I can promise you one thing — Scotland will be beautiful — though it may mean mud on your shoes."

"I never really scraped it off." Deborah smiled and took his hand. Together, they walked slowly into the house. □

"HE'S GOT TO GO!"

"WILLIE MILLER did *what*?" Gordon Brookes asked incredulously of the white-haired lady sitting in front of his desk.

Miss Rose sniffed.

"He pinched my bottom!" she repeated, glaring at Gordon as though it were his fault. "Well, really, Doctor Brookes, I don't know what things are coming to. Would you believe it, I even caught him putting a tot of whisky in his cocoa last night! Said it helped him sleep!"

She shuddered.

"You'll have to do something, Doctor. This used to be a nice, respectable home for retired ladies and gentlemen, but since that old reprobate arrived, it's become a — a den of iniquity!"

by
SARAH
BURKHILL

Gordon sighed. He was beginning to feel that taking Willie Miller in as a temporary guest had been the biggest mistake of his life.

On top of the complaints from the residents, he'd had the job of explaining to the board of administrators why Miltonbridge Old People's Home, which could cater for a *maximum* of 20 residents, now boasted 21.

"What else could I have done?" he'd asked Lady Dorothy, the chairwoman. "The old boy's flat is being modernised, and the social work department couldn't find any place else for him to go . . .

"So I've put him in that vacant staff-room on the ground floor," he'd added. "After all, it's only for a couple of weeks."

Unfortunately, the brevity of Willie's stay cut no more ice with the board than it did with the residents of Miltonbridge.

His thoughts returning to the problem of the moment, Gordon smiled placatingly at Miss Rose.

"I'm terribly sorry you've been subjected to this, Miss Rose. I'll speak to Willie again, and I'm sure this morning's — er — episode — won't be repeated. Willie was annoyed at having to come to the home, and I expect that's why he's making things so difficult.

Miss Rose pursed her lips.

"Probably knew all his evil ways would be discovered, if he lived amongst decent people," she declared knowingly. "Drinking, gambling — womanising! It's a wonder he hasn't been struck down!"

Gordon bit his lip to disguise a smile, and nodded solemnly.

"Quite right, Miss Rose, quite right."

H E broke off and stared at her for a moment.
Given something to do, perhaps Miss Rose and the others would have less time for complaining about Willie, and that would be at least one problem off his shoulders.

"I wonder, Miss Rose — don't you think that it's maybe our duty to take Willie in hand while he's here? Reform him, so to speak?"

"Hmmph! It would take an angel to reform that one," she said sourly.

"Exactly!" Gordon pounced. "That's why I thought you might have a word with him, Miss Rose. You know the sort of thing: make friends with him, try to get him to see the error of his ways. I'm sure with your good example, Willie could become quite a pillar of the community by the time he leaves us."

Miss Rose beamed. "Do you really think so?"

She considered the matter. "Yes, Doctor Brookes, you could be right. I'll speak to the others about it, and we could all help. As you say, it's only our Christian duty to try!"

Filled with her new-found missionary zeal, Miss Rose departed to work a miracle.

At the end of the first week, Gordon realised that there had been no more complaints — indeed, by the second week, Willie and the others actually appeared to be on friendly terms.

Gordon chuckled. Awkward Willie might be, but he was no match for Miss Rose once she got started. Why, he had even stopped badgering Vicki Morris, the social worker, for news of the flat's progress.

Thinking about Vicki, Gordon wondered if he might perhaps call round to see her — just to keep her up to date with the situation.

After all, he thought, carefully combing his hair and adjusting his tie, she'd gone to a lot of trouble over Willie. It would be nice to show her that somebody else was taking an interest.

"Anything good on?" he asked on his way out, popping his head round the door of the television lounge.

It was unusually crowded for that time of day.

"Shush!" Miss Rose commanded imperiously, turning to frown at him.

Gordon stared at her, wondering if she'd been at Willie's whisky. Miss Rose had never told anyone to "shush" in all her 72 years.

"She's two up on a cross treble," Willie confided in a whisper. "If Hielan' Laddie wins, she stands to get three pounds, forty-seven.

"Look, that's him in the black and purple, running fourth just now."

Gordon looked at the screen to which 21 pairs of eyes were riveted.

"Come on, Hielan' Laddie, come on!" Miss Rose shrieked, slapping her knitting needle against the arm of her chair, and bouncing up and down.

The commentator's voice rose to a crescendo and the tension in the room mounted, only to be broken by twenty-one sighs as Veritas passed the winning post.

"Third place!" Miss Rose said in disgust. "Rotten old Scotch bag of bones, couldn't race a haggis!"

Gathering up her needles and wool, she calmly returned to the pink bedsocks she was knitting.

"Anyone else got a horse on before the three-fifteen?" Willie asked.

Twenty heads shook from side to side.

"Right!" he announced, turning down the volume. "Who's for a game of dominoes before the next race, winner takes the kitty?"

The tables were brought out, and 21 old people eagerly queued for a place.

WELL, where's the harm in that?" Vicki Morris asked when Gordon had related the events of the afternoon.

He struggled to find an answer.

"Well, actually, I don't suppose there *is* any harm in it," he agreed eventually. "As long as they don't gamble all their pensions away, I don't object in the slightest.

"But I know who *will* object," he went on. "Lady Dorothy and the rest of the board. She'd have a fit if she saw twenty-one residents of Miltonbridge trooping into the local bookie's!"

Gordon shuddered at the very thought, then shot Vicki a black look when she smiled.

"I don't know what you think is so funny. It's all your precious Willie Miller's fault. One way or another, he's done nothing but stir things up since he came to us."

Vicki nodded.

"Yes, I know what you mean. Willie's not always the easiest person to deal with."

Ignoring Gordon's raised eyebrows at this understatement, she went on. "Still, it'll all be over by the end of the week. I was just going to telephone you. The flat will be finished on Thursday, so Willie can move back the following day."

She smiled. "There! That should be good news for everyone!"

B UT when Gordon reported the good news later, Willie didn't look exactly overjoyed.

"Go home?" he repeated, scowling.

"Yes, that's what you want, isn't it?" Gordon went on.

Willie snorted.

"I don't see that what I want's got anything to do with it," he declared. "It's what you lot want — always has been. Hounding me from pillar to post. 'Go here, go there!'

"You'd think at my age a man would be entitled to a bit of peace, wouldn't you?" He turned to the others in the day-room.

"You certainly are, Willie." To Gordon's horror, Miss Rose agreed.

"The authorities think they can push old people around. It's about time someone did something about it!"

Gordon groaned inwardly. That was a challenge Willie would find hard to resist, and he didn't even try.

"I'm staying put!" he announced determinedly.

Gordon sighed.

"Willie, you can't stay here! There's no room for you!" And he explained, as patiently as he could, that the home was full, that taking him in, even for two weeks, had caused a lot of trouble. If Willie wanted to join them permanently, why didn't he put his name down on the waiting list, then maybe in a year . . . ?

No!

But his nice little flat, all newly done up?

No!

Gordon ran his fingers through his hair.

"Well, I'm sorry, Willie, but it can't be helped," he said firmly. "Rules are rules. You're going home on Friday and that's that! Miss Morris will come and collect you." ▶ *over*

FAMOUS WOMEN

ANNA PAVLOVA (1881-1931).

This Russian ballerina was the most celebrated dancer of her time. She was born in St Petersburg and she studied at the Russian Imperial Ballet School.

Seven years later, after triumphs in "Swan Lake" and "Giselle," she was named prima ballerina.

She participated in Diaghilev's first Paris season, 1909, but, dissatisfied with her position in the company, she soon withdrew.

In 1910, with Mikhail Mordkin as her partner, she appeared with sensational success at the Palace Theatre, London, and Metropolitan Opera, New York City.

Forming her own company, Pavlova began the series of world tours which continued until her death. Before World War I, she returned regularly to the Marinsky Theatre, St Petersburg. She appeared in all the principal countries of North and South America, Europe, Africa and the Orient, bringing the art of ballet to numerous communities where it was unknown and inspiring many young dancers.

She made her home in London with her husband and manager, Victor Dandre. She died January 23, 1931, at The Hague.

Pavlova's repertoire consisted chiefly of classic ballets, including "Chopiniana," "Don Quixote" and "Coppelia." Her favourite was "Giselle." Her superb performance of the famous solo, "The Dying Swan," created for her in 1905 by Michel Fokine, was legendary.

Through her personal genius and her courageous example, she inspired a whole generation of dancers, from Australia to Finland. Her service to ballet and her influence on the artistes who followed were inestimable.

Willie refused to answer, merely glowering at Gordon from under his bushy white eyebrows.

THE next day, however, Willie seemed to have accepted the inevitable, for there was no further mention of his staying on.

In fact, everything remained remarkably quiet for the rest of the week.

It was just as he'd thought, Gordon decided. With Willie's influence broken, it would be no time at all before Miltonbridge returned to normal.

"Everything set, then?" Vicki asked, when she arrived on the Friday morning.

Gordon nodded, and smiled at her, wondering if the end of Willie's association with the home would mean the end of Vicki's visits. He hoped not.

"The housekeeper packed Willie's trunk this morning," he told her, "and he's waiting in the day room. I thought I'd go back with you, just in case — well, just in case," he finished lamely. There was no point in worrying her about Tuesday's declaration.

Gordon led the way downstairs and peered into the front room. Willie's trunk sat by the door, but Willie wasn't with it.

"Where's he gone?" Gordon asked the housekeeper. "I told him to stay here until Miss Morris fetched him."

Mrs Baker wrung her hands and coughed nervously.

"Er, he's outside, Doctor," she said. "Actually, they — they're *all* outside. I think there's going to be trouble."

"Trouble? What do you mean, trouble?" Vicki asked.

But Gordon had already thrown open the front door. Twenty-one people, banners waving, had positioned themselves across the lawn.

"All right, what's going on?" he demanded.

Miss Rose stepped forward importantly.

"Speaking as the elected chairperson of MAC — that's the Miltonbridge Action Committee," she explained graciously, "I must tell you that the residents are unanimous in their decision to strike until Mr William Miller is guaranteed a permanent place in the home."

A round of applause greeted her announcement, and the others waved their banners aloft, displaying the legend, "One Out, All Out."

Gordon stared at the scene before him, motionless, until Vicki Morris nudged him.

"Hadn't you better do something?" she suggested. "It's starting to rain — they'll all get soaked."

Back in his office, Gordon looked from Vicki to the esteemed visitor who now occupied his leather chair.

"So you see, Lady Dorothy," he finished, "there was nothing else

Fishin'

GROWING in the river,
    Tall rushes quiver,
Where it's clear and cool
Swimming in a pool.
Tiny minnows flit.
Warm sunbeams hit,
Lancing as a spear
Through water sparkling clear,
Reflecting two young faces,
Freckled, brown, with treacly traces.
Small hands eager, steady,
Holding jam-jar at the ready.
Spreadeagled all the day
On a bank of new-mown hay.
Now, advancing years may force
Our lives on a slower course,
But there's no harm in wishin'
For the days when we went fishin'.
           — Katherine MacIntyre.

we could do but let Willie back in again."

Lady Dorothy's expression suggested that *she* could have thought of several things, one of which, he suspected, was strangling a certain medical man who had been the cause of all her troubles.

"Is there really no way Willie could stay on?" Vicki asked, without much hope.

Lady Dorothy's eyebrows shot up.

"He doesn't *want* to stay on," she insisted. "He didn't want to come here originally, and he's only started all this to make trouble. He's just a thoroughly awkward, perverse old man!"

Vicki shook her head.

"You're wrong, Lady Dorothy. He's just a very lonely old man."

She pointed out of the window to the bench where Willie sat alone, gazing out over the garden.

"That flat Willie's in now was one my department found for him two years ago. Before that, he was a gardener over at the Thornley Estate, then when the place was sold for redevelopment —" She shrugged. "Well, Willie had to go, and so did his tied cottage, unfortunately."

S HE turned away from the window and faced the other two.
"Can you imagine what it's like for him, living in a poky little flat in town, with no garden to work in and no friends around him, his only real interest in life the television and a few pence each way on a horse?"

"And then he comes here, makes a few friends, gets settled in," Gordon finished for her. "Of course he doesn't want to leave!"

They were silent for a moment, then Lady Dorothy sniffed.

"Well, I don't know what you expect me to do about it," she began defensively. "If it were within my power to let Willie stay, then of course I would — the constitution says that we can't have more than twenty residents."

A slow grin spread across Gordon's face.

"But it *is* within your power to hire staff, Lady Dorothy?" he asked. "You don't have to consult the rest of the board about that?"

She frowned suspiciously.

"No — but what's that got to do with Willie?"

Gordon moved over to the window.

"You know, that garden really is in a shocking state," he announced conversationally. "The two boys who come in from the village haven't been able to cope."

Lady Dorothy smiled benignly.

"That's exactly what I was thinking when I came up the drive, Gordon," she said at once. "But it's so difficult to find good resident staff these days.

"You wouldn't happen to know anyone, would you?"

WILLIE paced up and down the office, tapping his folded newspaper against his leg.

"Well, I don't know about that," he said, rubbing his chin thoughtfully. "I'd have to give it a lot of thought."

"You would be doing us a great favour, Mr Miller," Lady Dorothy said meekly. "I knew the Thornley gardens well, and Miltonbridge would count itself very lucky indeed to have your services.

"It wouldn't have to be a full-time job, just a little bit of tidying up when you feel able," she went on. "And, of course, the two boys would be under your orders."

Willie scratched his head.

"Well, all right then," he said with a great show of reluctance. "Seeing as how you put it like that, I'll stay on.

"In fact, I could have a look this afternoon. See what needs done."

Hardly bothering to hide his enthusiasm now, Willie made for the door. Vicki's sigh of relief was audible.

Then he stopped and turned back.

"Er, fancy a wee flutter, your ladyship?" he asked, thrusting his paper under Lady Dorothy's nose. "There's a filly called Potty Dotty running in the three-forty-five. I could put ten pence on for you, if you like."

Moorland Peace

THE sky above is azure blue,
　Partly powdered with fleecy white,
The background moors are heather-clad,
　Patterned in purple carpets bright,
They slope to greens of ling and trees
　Varied in shape and colouring.
A lake reflects the blue of sky,
　Trickling streamlets laugh and sing
As gurgling past their rocks they move,
　Spanned by many a rustic bridge;
There's beauty here and perfect peace
　Beneath — beside — each moorland ridge,
A peace that Nature can bestow
　On those who come her ways to know.

— *Margaret Comer.*

Gordon closed his eyes and grimaced, awaiting the explosion. To his surprise, however, Lady Dorothy took the paper and studied the racing section carefully.

"At odds of fifteen to one?" she said eventually. "Not likely!"

"No," she went on, "I'd go for Mister Big. Did you see him last time out at Newmarket? He was beaten by a nose then, but there's no competition today. He's a certainty!"

Gordon stared after the two of them as they went downstairs. Then he turned to Vicki.

"Well, can you beat that!" he said incredulously.

"If Willie Miller's money is on it, probably not!" She laughed.

Gordon shook his head, then he found himself laughing too.

He put a hand on Vicki's shoulder. Now that everyone else's problems had been ironed out, it was about time he attended his own! □

by IAN WILSON ROMANCE-

THE Trattoria Maria had been very busy all evening, but now the customers were drifting away into the velvety warmth of an Italian evening.

Only one young couple remained, with eyes only for each other, a shiny new engagement ring sparkling on the girl's finger.

Paulo Merlini, who owned the small restaurant, was playing his guitar and singing a plaintive Neapolitan love song just for them.

Afterwards he came into the kitchen grinning at me.

"Ah, young love, so beautiful to see, don't you think so, Elena? That couple, they make me feel quite jealous, but I'm so happy for them."

"Love is wonderful at any age, Paulo," I replied.

He half-smiled, unsure of my reaction.

"I believe that under that reserve of yours, there's a romantic heart beating. Perhaps I shall find out one day?" In his question there was much impatience and frustration at my refusal to completely relax with him. In the months I'd been working for Paulo, we'd built up a strong friendship, nothing out of place, until the incident a few days ago which had put us both on guard.

For a moment Paulo looked as if he wanted to say something more, but suddenly changed the subject.

"That young English couple enjoyed their meal. They'd like to thank the cook personally, so you'd better go and see them."

"Yes, Paulo."

The young man addressed me in faltering Italian.

"It's all right," I told them. "I'm English, too."

"Thank goodness." The young man laughed. "Six months of Italian evening classes and I still can't speak the language well."

"The only way to learn is to live here, as I do," I said.

"Oh, we'd love to live here, wouldn't we, Mike." The girl sighed. "Stresa is such a lovely place, and the people are so kind. But that's only a dream, I suppose. No doubt we'll be glad to find our feet on English soil again — most travellers are."

Italian Style

Mike nodded his agreement. "But that meal was excellent. And cooked by an Englishwoman, too," he added with a grin.

"Yes, I suppose you do find it rather surprising to find someone like me in the Trattoria Maria." I spoke light heartedly. "I sometimes wonder myself what I'm doing here."

"Where is your home?" asked the girl, looking at me expectantly, but I hesitated.

Home, I thought, how hollow the word sounds. I found myself faced with that dreadful feeling of being pulled between past and present loyalties as the events of last year flashed through my mind.

★ ★ ★ ★

Until the day I met Raymond Price, I'd given little thought to any emotional involvement, I was much too busy working.

I was in my late twenties. High qualifications from catering school had led to some interesting cooking jobs, but none gave me the fulfilment I longed for, so I was restless.

Perhaps I'd been working so hard I'd forgotten there were other things in life apart from my job, like a little romance; and that's where Ray fitted in nicely.

Our first meeting was a touching of hands as we both reached out for the same potted geranium in a London suburb garden centre.

"You must have it." He smiled.

"But I couldn't, your hand was on it first."

"Only because I have a longer reach."

"You're sure?"

"As long as you give it a good home."

"All right," I promised.

"I'm here most Sundays. Perhaps we'll meet again, you can give me a report on the plant," he teased.

The next week I fooled myself into believing that my interest in returning to the garden centre was purely floral. The extra beat of my heart when we met, however, told me otherwise. Soon we were chatting and our friendship began from that moment.

A S the weeks went by, my life took on a new dimension. Ray was an interesting companion, fun to be with, yet why did I have the impression that he was keeping something from me?

He knew all about me, yet my interest in him was subtly brushed aside. I was being allowed to know as much as he wanted me to, which somehow made him all the more unattainable.

It was obvious he wanted nothing more than a casual relationship and although I'd hoped for something deeper, I realised I had to be content with matters as they were. After all, we were good friends, and spent many happy evenings together.

The meal we'd had in a riverside hotel near Maidenhead had been particularly delightful. Ray was in a jovial mood, charming and attentive as usual, yet his eyes were thoughtful.

"Helen, I've something to tell you," he finally said.

"Sounds serious," I teased.

"I'm going away for four weeks," he told me bluntly.

"What? Where to?" I tried not to show how upset I was.

"The Far East, Singapore."

"What for?" I was curious — he'd never mentioned that he travelled.

"Business reasons. The firm I work for in the city is seeking more investment abroad."

I was disappointed but controlled my feelings.

"Four weeks isn't very long, we'll be back together in no time."

Ray smiled, though I noticed he wouldn't meet my eyes.

"Yes, of course."

"Where are you flying from and when?" I asked.

"Heathrow. Nine o'clock. Thursday night."

"I promise I'll think of you right at that moment. But that's only

three days away," I said miserably. "Shall I see you before you go,
Ray?"

" 'Fraid not, love, I'll be too busy," he replied casually.

I HADN'T intended to see Ray off, but thought I'd give him a
surprise. Anyway, Heathrow was only a few miles from where I
lived.

Of course when I arrived I hadn't bargained for the seething mass
of people, nor had I asked Ray what airline he was travelling with.

I sought out the most likely and inquired at the information desk.
The young woman smiled pleasantly, and turned to her computer.

"Mr Raymond Price, you said."

"Yes."

"Here we are then." She smiled. "Mr Price and his wife checked in
half an hour ago. They have half an hour before their flight is called,
shall I call them for you?"

"No thanks, it's all right," I said, feeling numb with shock.

I was back home before the tears fell.

I lived with my older sister and her husband and they handled my
crisis admirably.

While Alastair made a strong pot of tea, Margaret comforted me,
coaxing me to tell her what had happened.

"You weren't to know," Margaret said sympathetically.

"That's no excuse!" I exclaimed. "I should have done, all the signs
were there that Ray was hiding something, yet I was too flattered by
his attentions to think clearly. What hurts is his deceitfulness."

"You'll soon forget him," Margaret assured me. "Your holiday's
due soon. Getting away will do you the world of good."

"Yes, it can't come quick enough for me now." I sighed.

"I'll see you off at Heathrow," she offered.

I was grateful for her company until my flight was called. I hadn't
relished walking round the airport on my own with thoughts of Ray
still on my mind.

Sitting in the aircraft, looking down on London, I thought of how
happy Margaret and Alastair were. Perhaps I was jealous of them,
just a little, for whatever Ray had done, he'd taught me that life had
more to offer than a satisfying job.

I'd chosen my holiday well. Stresa was in a delightful setting on the
shores of Lake Maggiore in Northern Italy.

Narrow cobbled streets were lined with cafés and shops, a pretty
lakeside promenade and gardens, elegant eighteenth century houses
with flower-decked balconies — the town had a kind of mystical
quality.

I felt strangely at home in this delightful place. Evening classes had
perfected my Italian so communicating was easy. I had the feeling the
Italians were impressed by someone who took the trouble to learn
their language; it was a compliment to them in a way, I suppose.

There was so much to do in and around Stresa, so many things to
see, but the heat tempered my activities. Besides, it was pleasant to

sit in one of the cafés and watch the world go by.

My favourite was the Trattoria Maria, where the coffee was excellent, the cream cakes delicious and there was music provided by the owner. Paulo Merlini played the guitar and sang nostaligic Neapolitan love songs.

As the days passed, I knew I was having a love affair with Italy.

The people were so friendly it was a joy to wander about and chat to the locals. I'd soon become a regular visitor to the Trattoria Maria and I got to know Paulo quite well. His eyes lit up when he saw me.

"Coffee and cream cake again?" he'd ask.

"Yes please."

"You are a good customer. While you are drinking your coffee, I shall sing you another song." His eyes twinkled with mischief. "Not everyone appreciates my singing but I know you do. As you see, like most Italians, I'm a romantic at heart. What else could I be in this beautiful country?"

WHAT a delightful man Paulo was. When the trattoria was quiet we had long conversations.

"How d'you come to speak such perfect English?" I asked one day.

"Because of my English mother. She was a young nurse with the British Army in Italy in 1945. My father Piero ran the trattoria then. One evening this nurse came in with some soldiers, off duty. For Piero it was love at first sight, and he pursued my mother until 1951 when they married."

"How lovely." I sighed, but Paulo was frowning.

"They'd almost given up hope of having children until I was born." He smiled a little sadly. "But when I was only eighteen my parents were killed in a landslide on the ski slopes."

"Oh, Paulo, I'm sorry."

"It was sad, but I had to go on, so I continued running the trattoria." He smiled, shaking off his pensive mood.

"And a handsome man like you has never married?" I teased him.

"What girl would have me?" Paulo declared. "You see I'd be accused of loving the Trattoria Maria first and the girl second."

"Oh, Paulo, you're joking." I laughed.

He gave me that devil-may-care grin of his.

"Well, maybe just a little. One day, perhaps, I'll find someone I can love more than the trattoria.

"But what about you, Elena? You come in here every day and I know little about you. Is there no handsome man in your life?"

"No-one."

"Ah yes." He smiled. "Maybe that's why you look so sad sometimes."

I told him I didn't mean to.

"My work is my life really."

"And what do you do?" he asked curiously.

"I'm a cook."

Paulo's eyes lit up with interest.

"How would you like to see how I make the best pasta in Stresa?"

"Very much."

So I made the first of many visits in to his kitchens to learn the art of pasta making and all those wonderful sauces that go with it. I even tried a hand myself and Paulo seemed pleased with my work.

"Ah, Elena, a few weeks more here and I shall have a rival," he teased.

"But I'm going back to London soon," I reminded him.

"Ah yes, to the cold and the rain." He sighed. "You could stay and work for me."

"Oh, Paulo, you're teasing me." I laughed.

"No, Elena I wouldn't do that. I need someone reliable to help me, not a cook who gets all temperamental and walks out on me because I criticise this or that."

"Perhaps you should stop criticising." I smiled.

"I criticise things because the trattoria must set a high standard or I lose all my customers."

"I could be temperamental, too."

"No, I'm a good judge of character, I know you'd stay calm under pressure," he assured me.

"But I can't, I'm sorry, London's my home and —"
I couldn't admit how tempted I was by his offer.

"You're right, I shouldn't have asked, I'm sorry. When do you go home?"

Wet Welcome

TWO little boys that once I knew
  Had a habit very naughty,
They'd knock on knockers — then run
    away —
  They thought it highly sporty.
They always came by as they left their
    school
  So we thought of a way to get
    them.
We hid with a bucket of water cold,
  When they knocked we decided to
    wet them.
A knock resounded — we opened and
    flung,
  We knew they'd be quick, but we
    quicker —
And so we were — but alas, alas!
  On our step stood a dripping vicar.
    — *Margaret Comer.*

"Tomorrow afternoon, I'm afraid, I shall miss Stresa . . ."

"You must come back here this evening and I'll cook something very special for you."

"Thanks, Paulo, I look forward to that."

I spent the rest of the day crowding my mind with memories. I sailed to the Borromean Islands on the steamer and visited the Isola Bella Palace and gardens.

I'd thought my mind was made up about going home; instead I was floundering with indecision. I just knew I could work alongside Paulo, the trattoria had the sort of atmosphere I'd enjoy.

But, after my disastrous friendship with Ray, my emotions were still in a bruised state and Paulo was an attractive man. Why else had I been drawn back to the trattoria day after day?

WHEN I returned in the evening, Paulo was as good as his word, the meal he cooked for me was delightful. And the delicious pasta was accompanied by a bottle of Paulo's best wine. It all made my last evening quite perfect.

Paulo insisted on walking me back to the hotel afterwards.

"I shall miss you, Elena," he admitted as we strolled along the promenade.

"No you won't," I replied. "You'll soon find another Englishwoman to charm, and I'll be forgotten."

"No, Elena, I know it's an old saying, but I've never met any woman quite like you before. Please stay."

"Oh, Paulo." I sighed. "I wanted you to ask me again so I could say yes this time. You see, I wasn't sure I believed you the first time. All right, I'll stay, but not permanently, think of it as a trial period."

So that's how I came to be working for Paulo Merlini and I quickly established a niche for myself, cooking, sometimes waiting at tables, even buying the vegetables from the local market. I was delighted for, at last, I'd found a job which gave me the fulfilment I longed for.

Though Paulo and I had an excellent relationship and worked closely together, that was as far as it went. Paulo never tried to alter the balance by hinting at anything deeper, and both of us seemed to be content to keep it that way.

Then came the incident which changed everything. With the trattoria closed for the daily afternoon siesta, Paulo and I travelled on the cable car to the summit of the Mottarone mountain.

I was almost dizzy with excitement, the clear air, the wild flowers, and the view . . . sheer mountains plunging into the Lombardy Lakes far below . . .

"Oh, Paulo." I gasped in excitement. "This is beautiful. Thank you for bringing me up here."

He gave me an appreciative smile.

"It's worth it just to see the enjoyment in your eyes, such a change from those looks of sadness when your mind is far away."

Paulo shook his head sadly.

"You're like a beautiful rose, Elena — stubbornly refusing to blossom in the warmth of Italian sunshine because your roots are still deep in the rain and cold of London. How long have you been here now?"

"Nearly a year."

"But you're still not sure where you want to be — Stresa or London — you should make up your mind."

"You should know what the English are like, Paulo, always longing for their homeland," I told him with a smile.

"Then perhaps what you need is a good reason for staying here."

"But I have so many."

Paulo smiled.

"The one I have in mind is very special. Remember I said I hoped to find someone who would mean more to me than the Trattoria Maria? Well, I've found you, Elena"

I felt my heart missing a beat. As Paulo reached out to draw me into his arms I almost yielded, but caution intervened, and I pulled myself away.

Paulo turned his back and walked several yards away from me.

"Oh, Paulo, I'm sorry." But I knew there was nothing I could say to relieve the pain my rejection had caused him.

"I'd hoped that after all this time we might mean more to each other than just friends." His voice was full of disappointment. "I remember the first day you walked into my place, looking quite lost, I fell in love with you then. I love you now.

"I'd hoped that one day you might return my love, but obviously I was wrong. Please forgive me."

"There's nothing to forgive." I turned away in case he saw the tears glistening in my eyes.

Few words were spoken on our return to Stresa, both of us realising that his admission had caused a shift in our relationship.

As days passed of strained conversation, a wariness of each other, I knew we could never be the same to each other again. Nor could there be a place for me at the trattoria any more.

Suddenly my life had reached crisis point emotionally. Soon I would have to make the decision about returning to London.

★　　　★　　　★　　　★

It was the young girl asking the question for the second time which brought me back to the present.

"Where is your home?"

I stood there, conscious of all the sounds about me which had been my security for so long. Paulo, Anna, Carla, their voluble Italian voices raised good humouredly. The atmosphere as usual was one of warmth and friendliness. Perhaps that's why I answered the girl's question so easily.

"Oh, I used to live in London, but this is my home now, I never want to be anywhere else."

Paulo, who had been clearing a table nearby, heard me and looked up, giving me an adoring look.

Later, when the trattoria was closed, we strolled along the lakeside promenade, the evening air heavy with the scent of flowers.

"So you've come to your senses at last," Paulo said with a smile.

"Yes, and I've that young couple to thank for reminding me what love is all about, sharing the joy of being close, living for each other, looking forward to the future.

"I do love you, Paulo, but couldn't admit it to myself. I've been so happy working with you I was scared that emotional involvement might complicate things."

Paulo sighed.

"Ah, at last *ma bella signorina* has lost some of her English reserve. Now you're becoming romantic, like an Italian."

As I slipped into Paulo's arms I knew I'd found what I'd denied myself for so long, my own very special place in Italy. □

F

IT was a miserable late-November day, and I took my lunchtime
sandwiches into the little day-room my firm have for their staff,
rather than venture out into the rain.

There's seldom anyone in the room, which just has a few chairs
and a table with magazines, but I prefer it to eating my lunch in the
canteen or the big office where I work, because you're away from the
telephone and the chatter, and can be quiet.

I valued quiet a lot just at that time. I wasn't feeling sociable or in
the mood for office gossip. So I was quite annoyed to discover
someone else was there ahead of me.

It was a young man who had recently joined the firm and whose
name I didn't know.

He was a lanky gangling lad with glasses and a forbidding expression. He looked up from his book at my arrival, seeming about as
pleased to see me as I was him.

I gave him a brief nod and sat down on the far side of the room,
which, as it was small, wasn't very far. Getting out the lunch Mum
had made me, and a magazine, I tried to settle down for half an hour
of peace.

The man didn't have any lunch with him and when I'd eaten a
couple of sandwiches, I began to feel uneasy. It seemed funny to be
eating alone.

I pushed my lunch-box across the table to him. "Want a sandwich?"

EVERYTHING

by
SYLVIA
WYNNE

TO OFFER

He blushed up to his ears and said shortly, "No thanks."

I'd have taken the tin back but I suddenly noticed the expression on his face. He was staring, positively wolfishly, at my pile of sandwiches.

"Go on," I said. "I've had all I want. I'll only throw the rest out. Mum always makes far too much."

He hesitated. "You mean that? That you'll throw them out?"

"Yes, of course. Go on, help yourself."

I watched while he nervously extracted a cheese sandwich from the foil. Then it was gone as if sucked into a vacuum cleaner. He was really hungry.

I made him finish the rest.

"That was great," he muttered. "I didn't have any breakfast."

"Doesn't your mum make you? Mine does," I said, smiling. There was something touching about a person being as ravenous as that.

"Haven't got one." He blushed rosy-red again.

"Can I get you a coffee from the machine?" he offered. As well as starving, he was obviously shy.

About to refuse, I realised he wanted to pay me back for the food, so I said yes, though I hated the thin machine coffee.

We sat and sipped at our plastic cups.

M Y name's Carla Shaw," I said chattily, trying to make my companion relax. It was obviously torture for him sitting here with me like this. I began to regret having come in here.

"Mine's Terry Waterman," he said. Then, with a mighty effort, "I work in the post-room. I've just started. You're in the general office, aren't you?"

"Yes, that's right. I've been here for about a year. Is this your first job?"

Painfully, we made conversation until it was time to go back to work.

Then Terry got up to go. "Thanks a lot for the sandwiches," he said in that awkward way of his. Another blush. "To be honest, I was really hungry."

I grinned. "I noticed." It occurred to me that in spite of his gaucheness, there was something rather nice about this boy.

"I'll maybe see you tomorrow," I said, and a sudden unexpected smile lit up his plain face.

"I'll look forward to that very much," he said in a funny old-fashioned way, and just about managed to get out of the room without knocking into anything.

When I told mum about Terry she smiled and said, "I'd better put some extra food in your lunch-box, then!"

I didn't think I could get him to accept it, but when it came to the point, he couldn't resist it, and polished off all my leftovers.

"You must think me an awful hog," he apologised. "Tomorrow *I'll* bring the lunch."

So we had a date? I let him get the horrible coffees, then I said, "Did you say you hadn't a mum? Want to tell about it?"

Terry had been beginning to lose some of his awful shyness, but now it came back.

"That's right. Nor any dad. Live on my own," he muttered.

Aghast, I drew the story out of him. He'd never known his father, not seen his mother for years, spent his teenage years in care, and now lived on his own in a bed-sitter.

"I keep spending all my money on books and not leaving enough for food," he admitted. "I want to make something of myself — don't want to be in a routine job all my life."

He looked across at me, and our eyes really connected. I could see in his face all the sadness and longing of an utterly lonely person. My heart turned over. Tears sprang into my eyes.

"You don't have to feel sorry for me," he burst out then, quite angrily.

"I wasn't," I said honestly. "I — oh, Terry!"

I reached across and touched his hand. I wanted to tell him something I almost never talked about now.

"I know a bit of what trouble is, too," I told him. "Last year my dad died in a terrible accident at the factory where he worked. Mum and I are on our own now."

Instantly, his hand gripped mine. "That's bad, that's really bad," he said.

We sat there staring at one another. Tears began to roll down my face, but I sniffed them back furiously.

Snowdrop

SNOWDROP — small, fragile flower —
Brightening winter's darkest hour,
Thrusting through the iron-hard ground,
Receiving welcome all around;
Showing, bravely, a snowflake face,
Edged about with soft, green lace,
Swaying, on such delicate stalks,
To beautify our winter walks.

— Gillian Riddle.

I couldn't start crying here or I'd never stop.

"I just wanted to tell you," I sniffed. And when Terry said, "I'm glad you did, Carla." There was a wealth of sympathy and understanding in his voice.

SO Terry and I became friends. We didn't talk about my father or his background again — somehow, we didn't need to.

But I found I could say anything I felt like to him, with the knowledge that he'd understand and take it seriously.

Most of my boyfriends were cheerful, hearty types who I fooled about and had fun with, but didn't really talk to. Dad's death had set up a weird barrier between us. The subject embarrassed them.

With Terry, I felt at ease. He talked quite naturally about all sorts of heavy things, relationships, people, death and that.

I used to go to his room which he'd fixed up in a totally original and amazing way, with no money but a lot of imagination. He said he got things off skips and in junk markets, and enjoyed it far more than just buying stuff in shops.

Travel firms gave him old posters. A radio and TV shop where he worked on Saturdays sold him a returned tape-deck and radio very cheap, and this was his most treasured possession. He introduced me to all sorts of music I'd never heard before, and we used to sit there in his room for hours just listening to tapes.

Christmas came along, and how I dreaded it. The first Christmas on our own without Dad.

"I want to go to bed on Christmas Eve and not wake up till it's time to go back to work," I told my mum fiercely.

"I wish we could do that. But it's got to be lived through," Mum said grimly. And I felt a heel, knowing how much worse it must be for her. She and Dad had been all the world to one another.

We got lots of invitations from neighbours, however, to join them. Their kindness amazed me. Finally Mum said, "I want a big party *here*. A Christmas dinner here in this house. I don't want to go out, I want to be in my own home, like always."

So we asked around, and finally found a collection of people who for one reason or another were glad not to have to cook a turkey. Either the wives were working or the dads were on shiftwork, or the kids had split-up parents and "steps" they didn't get on with.

They all gave Mum a subscription and she did the shopping and catering — she's good at that. She used to work at it, only since Dad's death she hasn't really been well enough.

It gave us both something to do, preparing for the meal. I quite enjoyed it. Anything was better than the dead dullness of the house in the evenings, with just Mum and me and a television set we hardly ever even bothered to switch on.

O N the day before we broke up at work for the holiday, it occurred to me to ask Terry what he was going to do.

Terry shrugged. "Nothing much, I guess. Read. Listen to tapes. Walk around."

"You mean you're not going anywhere?" Fancy me not thinking of him! "Well, for goodness sake, you are now. You're coming to us, Terry."

He demurred at first. He'd never been to our house. It had never occurred to me to ask him. I mean, he wasn't my boyfriend, there was nothing romantic between us at all, never had been.

I'd wondered about it at first, then stopped even considering it. I wasn't in the mood for romance anyway so this just-good-friends arrangement suited me fine. Since Dad died, I didn't seem to have any heart left.

So I gave Terry directions about how to get to our house, and he said he'd come up on his bike.

Everyone arrived at the appointed time, one o'clock, including Terry. All the guests gave us embarrassingly generous presents, saying in the size of their gifts, I suppose, what they hadn't been able to in words. The living-room was soon piled high. My face ached with smiling my thanks.

Suddenly I caught sight of Terry, standing in one corner of the room looking acutely miserable.

I made my way over to him through the throng. "Hello, love, come and have a glass of mulled wine," I offered. "Mum makes it. It's smashing."

Terry said in a strangled gulp, "I didn't bring you a present."

"So? I haven't got one for you either," I told him (untruthfully).

"I didn't think," he muttered. "Never been much of a one for presents. Didn't have the occasion."

"Well, we don't bother much either — all this shower is a bit embarrassing really," I comforted him, still lying. In fact, Mum and Dad and I used to go to town at Christmas, with stockings and secrets and all manner of nonsense. Of course I had a present for Terry tucked away, and so did Mum, but how could we give it to him now? I'd have to get word across to Mum before she came out with it before I could stop her.

"Come and meet my mum, anyway," I said quickly, and towed him across the room before he could protest. Under cover of sending him to get himself a glass of mulled wine from the sideboard, I whispered urgently to Mum.

"Oh, the poor child!" Mum said, understanding at once.

She went over to Terry and took him by the hand, and kissed his cheek warmly.

"Lovely to have you here," she said, and he did cheer up a little. No-one can resist my mum, she's a really lovely lady even now, when Dad's dying has taken most of her with him.

"I'm going to dish up now," she told me, and announced this to the assembled company. They surged into the dining-room and began taking their seats.

Terry and I exchanged glances.

"I'll help you," he said quickly. Before I could protest he was out in the kitchen asking Mum for an apron.

"I could carve if you like?" he offered. "Did hotel work once. You dish up the vegetables and sauces, Mrs Shaw, and Carla can take in the plates."

IT was really brilliant the way Terry got us organised — just like Dad used to. Soon everyone was served, and Terry whipped out two plates of turkey he'd been keeping hot.

"One for each of you two," he announced proudly. Our plates were piled with the choicest meat.

"Hey, what about you, son?" Mum demanded.

Terry looked quite surprised — he'd forgotten to do a plate for himself!

After the meal, everyone sat about saying how full they felt. The oldies collapsing on chairs and the settee were red-faced with food and drink. The young ones sprawled on the floor in front of the blaring telly oblivious to everything outwith that 20-inch square.

Suddenly, I felt really awful. All this food and drink and presents and noise. What did it all amount to? Christmas? Never! Christmas, for me, was gone for ever.

I crept out into the kitchen. Mum sat on a kitchen stool looking white with exhaustion.

She wasn't alone. Terry was at the sink confronting a bowlful of soapy water and a pile of plates and cutlery. He looked the most cheerful one of us there.

"I'll wash and you dry," he greeted me. "Mum, if you move off that stool I'll kill you! Right, Carla, let's get cracking!"

This was shy, diffident Terry? However, I didn't complain, but piled in, pausing only to give Mum a quick hug.

Mum, was it Terry had said? Cheeky!

We set the kitchen to rights, then put the kettle on for tea. Outside we dimly heard the sound of the company enjoying themselves, but we didn't envy them.

"You're a sensational cook, Mrs Shaw," Terry said, shy again now, handing her a cup of tea.

"Always liked to cook," Mum said. "Dad and I used to talk about starting a guest-house of our own in the country somewhere, only there wasn't the money. And there was Carla's future to think about."

"Did you want that?" I said, astonished. "You never said."

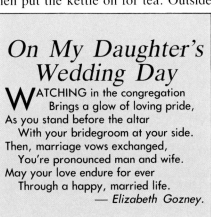

On My Daughter's Wedding Day

WATCHING in the congregation
Brings a glow of loving pride,
As you stand before the altar
With your bridegroom at your side.
Then, marriage vows exchanged,
You're pronounced man and wife.
May your love endure for ever
Through a happy, married life.

— *Elizabeth Gozney.*

But of course they wouldn't, would they — in case I hated the idea? They were the unselfish sort.

IT seemed like years before the last of the guests went. Terry made a pile of sandwiches for tea.

"Terry, you're a hero," I whispered in his ear as I lifted plates to take them through to the dining-room. "What should we have done without you? It's been a bit much for Mum, I'm afraid."

His face went absolutely radiant, that was the only word for it.

"What should *I* have done without *you?*" he returned.

Finally, dishes all done, Mum reappeared.

"I'd better be getting along," Terry said.

"You'll do no such thing!" Mum asserted. She was looking more like her old self.

She took Terry in her arms and gave him a great big hug.

"You're staying here tonight, my lad," Mum ordered. "No lonely bed-sitting-room for you — I won't hear of it after all you've done! Now, what about another cup of tea?"

I found the tape of Christmas carols we always used to play, which I'd hidden away, and put it on the stereo. Mum buried her face in her hands and sobbed her heart out, and Terry and I sat one on either side of her on the settee and held her tight.

We didn't speak. There wasn't any need of words. Terry and I were crying, too.

"I wish I'd brought you presents," Terry said wistfully, later on, when we were tidying up the lounge.

Mum said brusquely, "You brought what you could, son. You didn't come empty-handed. Who needs fancy slippers and dolls? The work you've done today was worth more than anything you could have bought us in a shop, and I know Daddy would have said the same."

"He would, too," I added soberly.

Mum said wistfully, "I do like to have a man about the house, and that's a fact."

"Why don't you get yourself that guest-house, Mrs Shaw. I'd willingly help you with it — I'd like that sort of work, not having a boss. Well — " That blush of his came up.

"I mean, you wouldn't be like a boss," he muttered. "And if Carla helped, too — "

"Got it all worked out, haven't you?" I said, grinning. But the idea had appeal.

Mum said slowly, "Well, I don't know, Terry. It would be a big decision." Her smile flashed out then. "It's certainly a thought, though, love. Thank you for the offer."

AFTER she'd gone to bed, Terry and I went out for a stroll. It was fresh and cold outside, and there was a big moon.

Terry took my arm and hugged it against him.

"Oh, Carla," he said, "I think you're the loveliest person in the whole world."

I gulped. Funny things were happening to that frozen heart of mine. Emotions I didn't expect ever to feel again were painfully stirring.

He pulled me to a halt, and put his cold hands on either side of my face. I held my breath.

Terry kissed me. His hands were cold but his lips were warm and searching, and sent tremors of wonder and delight through my whole body.

"I love you, Carla," Terry said almost in a groan. "I'm nothing and no-one and haven't a thing to offer anyone, but I love you more than anything else in the world."

"I love you, too," I whispered. I'd just discovered it was true. "And you do have something to offer; a pair of strong arms, a head with some sense in it, and a loving heart," I told him strongly. "That's not nothing, Terry . . ." □

JUST A LITTLE

WHEN Madame Yvonne opened her fashion boutique in Bramblegate, she couldn't have known of the pleasure it would give to old Mrs Robinson. Mrs Robinson had once owned a fashion boutique herself, only in those far-off days it had been known as a gown shop.

The new one filled a need in the old lady's life which nothing else could have filled. It was somewhere to go as she pottered around the small country town; something to admire, criticise and always be interested in.

There was no doubt that Yvonne (whose real name was Alice Banks) had taste. Mrs Robinson nodded her silvery head approvingly at the opening window display. Forsythia and orange-centred narcissi in a Chinese vase; and two exquisite evening dresses arranged with expert carelessness across a Queen Anne chair. One the misty blue of hyacinths in a woodland glade; the other the incredible green of early spring.

There was a suit, too, and a hat which looked like a froth of apple blossom beneath a curled plume, and was shaped like a heart.

The whole effect was a symphony to spring, and Mrs Robinson would have loved to go into the shop; she was aching to buy something new and exciting, for it was years since she'd had the pleasure of selecting a special outfit for herself. Special outfits, you see, needed a special occasion, and these didn't seem to occur any more, unless you counted funerals.

So Yvonne's boutique was the focal point of her morning

by
KATE CLAYTON

UNDERSTANDING

outing, which she took whatever the weather, being a great believer in fresh air and healthy activity.

Each day she forced herself to push her shoulders back and take two or three really deep breaths before she reached the end of her road. She felt fitter then and ready to take an interest in life.

When she returned to her little house, the one her son had persuaded her to move into when she was widowed, she would make herself a toasted sandwich and a cup of Ovaltine, and then settle down in her window seat to watch the world go by.

WATCHING the world go by had become another of her daily pleasures. She loved to observe people and wonder what they were doing with their lives. Sometimes she looked at very old ladies, like herself, and wondered if their feet hurt as much as hers did when she wore her smart shoes.

But, lately, she had found a new and exciting occupation, and this was watching the new young couple who had moved into the house opposite less than a month ago.

They were delightful! Young, gloriously in love and beautiful. Already they were smiling and saying good morning to her when they passed her house with the two little dogs — which they did every day. They both went out to work, she was sure, and she was longing for an opportunity to offer to help them by feeding the dogs or taking in parcels or whatever.

And then, one day, one of the dogs strayed into her front garden and started digging a hole. The young husband was after him like a shot.

"I'm so sorry," he mouthed to Mrs Robinson through the window.

Mrs Robinson went outside and they had a little chat about the training of dogs.

"Don't hit him," the old lady pleaded. "After all, he doesn't know any better."

"He does now!" Richard Halliday replied, giving the miscreant a sharp tap on the nose.

And then, because she was anxious to

keep him talking a bit longer, Mrs Robinson said, "Those two little dogs of yours must get lonely while you and your wife are out at work. Would you like me to pop across and feed them for you, and let them out from time to time?"

He smiled then and she saw that his blue eyes were thoughtful and kind. "Why don't you come over and have a cup of tea with Pam and me?" he suggested. "We could talk about it."

SO Mrs Robinson went over. Pam was as nice and thoughtful as her husband, apart from being rather shy and a bit inhibited at first, but the three of them got on fine.

"The dogs live outside," Pam said when the shyness had worn off. "Richard has built them an all-weather kennel with a flap door to keep out the cold and a carpet to lie on. But they could do with a bit of company when we're at work."

After this, things worked out well between them, and Mrs Robinson found her days — which had occasionally seemed a bit overlong — seemed fuller and happier. With Yvonne's boutique to inspect, the two dogs to feed and her garden and house to tend, life was richer than it had been for a long time.

The two youngsters seemed to have taken to her as much as she had taken to them. Pam would often pop across with cooking queries and seemed pleased when Mrs Robinson offered bits of old-fashioned advice.

Richard was kindness itself — fixing fuses which blew, unsticking jammed windows, replacing lamps which the old lady could only reach by standing on a chair (which he said she must never do). In return, Mrs Robinson lent them her empty garage to keep their garden tools in, and kept their spare key on a hook in her kitchen.

Never had a summer sped so swiftly nor so pleasantly, and she decided that growing old wasn't such a dismal business after all!

And then one morning, while she was brushing her hearthrug across the clothes line in her back garden, old Miss McPherson from next door, poked her grey head over the dividing fence.

She came straight to the point. "I wouldn't get too friendly with that pair across the road," she began darkly, jerking her thumb in the direction of Richard's house.

"Why not?"

"They're not what they appear to be," came the reply. "If you know what I mean."

"I don't," Mrs Robinson said.

There was a significant silence, then the other mouthed with exaggerated grimaces, "They're not *married*. I found out from the Postie. You can't hide *that* sort of thing from the Postie!"

"What sort of thing?"

"Not being married, of course. They call it co-habiting, but I call it disgusting." She sniffed self-righteously.

SUDDENLY, some of the sunshine seemed to go out of the morning for Mrs Robinson. She wished she'd used her new-fangled vacuum cleaner and not brought her hearthrug out of the house at all, then she wouldn't have become engaged in this distasteful conversation with her elderly neighbour, whom she'd never really cared for.

But it was too late now. Miss McPherson was waiting for a reply, and Mrs Robinson knew she had to make one.

First of all she brushed her rug so vigorously she was panting and they were both enclosed in a cloud of dust, and then, although her heart was positively thumping against her ribs, she said as evenly as she could, "I'm sure you're mistaken."

Miss McPherson gave a sort of choking snort, which might well have been caused by the dust. "Why don't you ask them?" she spluttered. "You're thick enough with them."

"I wouldn't dream of doing such a thing," Mrs Robinson said with dignity. "Pam and Richard are good friends of mine, and even if what you say is true, it doesn't alter the fact. They've been very kind to me."

Miss McPherson's jutting chin, with its big black wart, trembled. "Have you no moral standards?" she said in a scandalised voice. "Do you approve of living in sin?"

"No . . . of course not," poor Mrs Robinson protested, recalling with a shudder her strict Methodist upbringing. "B . . . but you can't . . . you can't just condemn people without knowing the full facts."

Miss McPherson sniffed again, and then, quite literally, she disappeared from her side of the fence, rather like a Punch and Judy act.

MRS ROBINSON went back into the house and made herself a strong cup of tea to which she added a teaspoonful of cooking sherry. She felt quite limp as she slowly sipped her restorative, for she had never dreamed that her two young friends were anything but a respectable married couple.

She still liked them as much as ever, but in a curious, inexplainable way, she was disappointed in them.

That afternoon, as she was using her new steam iron, it packed up on her. She knew Richard would have fixed it in next to no time, but she hesitated to take it across to him. Her new-found knowledge inhibited her to an alarming extent.

How could you accept favours from friends if you privately disapproved of them? Yet what right had she, or anyone else, to disapprove of such a warm-hearted, lovable couple? It was just that her generation found it hard to accept such totally different values.

She passed a restless night trying to come to terms with the situation. She felt she ought to do something but she didn't know what to do. She had a terrible feeling she should show her disapproval in some way, but she knew that she couldn't do it.

The next morning she took her steam iron into the electricity shop which was next to Yvonne's, and had to pay what she considered an extortionate amount to have it repaired. Richard wouldn't have allowed her to pay a penny.

THE nights were beginning to draw in now, and Mrs Robinson felt suddenly sad because her lovely summer was at an end. She was sure, however, she wouldn't be as lonely as usual in the coming winter, because when the little house across the way was lit up, she could see Pam and Richard moving about behind their undrawn curtains.

Quite often they paused in the window and waved to her, and, as she acknowledged the friendly gesture with a return wave, a trickle of warmth would flow right through her body.

She wished desperately she could banish the feeling of censure which lurked occasionally deep down inside her. She even prayed about it sometimes. Who was she to sit in judgment over others?

She made a point of being specially nice to both Richard and Pam whenever they met, and then hated herself in case she was being hypocritical. Suppose they noticed some change in her manner?

She didn't enjoy her visits to the boutique as much as previously either. Life seemed to have gone stale, although Yvonne's window display at the present time was a rhapsody to autumn with copper beech leaves, golden brown chrysanthemums and clumps of purple heather.

Mrs Robinson, fumbling in the recesses of her handbag for her glasses, considered it could have been even better if a stuffed pheasant or even a ptarmigan had been placed amidst the heather. And then she saw Pam coming out of the shop.

"Hello, Mrs Robinson."

"Hello, Pam. Not at work this morning?"

Pam looked embarrassed. "I . . . I've got a day off to do some shopping."

"That sounds exciting. Have you bought something from Yvonne's?"

"Actually . . . I have," Pam said. "But I've had to leave it for an alteration." She smiled at Mrs Robinson then and her eyes were especially bright. "When it's ready perhaps you'd like to come across and tell me what you think about it?"

"I'd like that," the old lady said, and wondered why she'd never noticed before the inner radiance which seemed to exude from the young woman.

When Pam had gone on her way, Mrs Robinson returned to her scrutiny of the shop window. Yvonne was on her knees, her mouth full of pins, deftly arranging a dress.

And *what* a dress! Cut with a line of extreme mature elegance in finest wool, shading from fuchsia to amethyst. The colour which went so well with silvery hair and wrinkles, sighed Mrs Robinson.

She would simply have loved to buy that dress, but it seemed pointless. When would she have an occasion to wear such a garment?

L ATER, however, when she and Pam were enjoying a cup of coffee together she was able to let herself go over the girl's purchase.

"It's exquisite," she breathed, stroking the material with expert fingers. "Pure classic. It will never date or go out of shape. Is it for a special occasion?"

Pam's face went bright scarlet. "It's . . . it's for a wedding," she said at last, a bit breathlessly.

"I haven't been to a wedding for over twenty years," Mrs Robinson said in a far-off dreamy voice. "I just keep going to funerals now." Her eyelashes glittered and her voice trembled ever so slightly. "I *love* weddings."

"Well . . . Richard and I hope you will come to this one . . ." Pam began, and then she stopped. "Maybe you won't wish to . . . you see it won't be in church . . ."

Mrs Robinson felt her stomach begin to churn. She realised the moment was one of significance, and she was fearful of spoiling it. She moistened her lips and smiled at Pam, totally unaware of the wealth of understanding in her faded blue eyes.

"You know!" the younger woman burst out, and she went deathly white. "You know, about Richard and me. Don't come to our wedding if you'd rather not. My folk aren't coming anyway . . ."

Before Mrs Robinson could speak, Pam brushed away the gathering tears. "I wanted to tell you right at the beginning, but Richard thought it better not. He . . . he thought you wouldn't understand. It's surprising the number of people who don't even in this day and age."

She stopped, fumbled for a hankie and blew her nose. "We didn't think the divorce would be so . . . so clear-cut. We thought we might have to wait for ever. But it's all over now, and we're going to get married even though it can't be in church."

Mrs Robinson was intensely aware of the young vulnerability of her companion. She knew exactly the sort of girl Pam was — ashamed and unhappy despite her defiance of the conventions. Neither of the young couple was the type Miss McPherson had inferred, and now by some miracle, they were free!

Mrs Robinson's romantic heart was brimming over.

"I shall most certainly want to come to your wedding," she said firmly, putting her arms round the prospective bride and kissing her warmly. "I've been longing for a special occasion, and what could be more special than a wedding between you and Richard?" □

Distant Moors

T HE scalloped outline of the moors
  A welcome warm for me includes,
Those lonely headlands seem to beckon me,
  A series of sweet solitudes;
They with their sloping, verdant valleys, green
  And with their lilting, trickling streams,
In calm, majestic awe express for me
  A land of quiet, peaceful dreams.
  — *Margaret Comer.*

The White

WHEN Peggy Martin glanced up from her seat in the hotel lounge and saw the elderly man come in, she immediately began to conjecture where she had seen him before. There was something familiar about the shape of his head and the deep-set eyes that stirred her memory.

She watched him sit down in a far corner, away from the other guests, open up his paper and start to read. Obviously a retiring type, she felt an immediate relationship with him, for she was also a quiet, reserved person.

And that set off another search in her mind, but there was no response.

Peggy had arrived by train from Glasgow that very morning at the Highland village of Glenbreck which she had known so well when she was young. She had come on a nostalgic visit and here she was, dinner over, in a purple dress that suited a white-haired woman of seventy, already relaxed and beginning to recall those distant days of childhood.

Peggy had been taken to Glenbreck by her parents for their annual holiday almost every year of her childhood. Not then, the luxury of a hotel, but the simple delights of a cottage with everyone lending a hand so that they could all spend as many hours as possible out in the pine-scented air.

It had been the kind of place where families came year after year at the same time, with the result that friendships were formed, lay dormant for a year, then revived with even greater strength.

Now, Peggy was remembering the little group of them, growing into the springtime of their youth, running around on hired bicycles, playing tennis or climbing the heather hills.

Suddenly, Peggy knew who the man was — Billy Wood, one of the regulars to Glenbreck all those years ago. The years and the responsibilities of life had inevitably changed him, but then so had it with everyone!

She smiled at the remembrance of Billy. He had been an attractive youth, full of fun and kindly with it. He had been everybody's favourite. The thought of meeting him again was creating in Peggy a warm, comforting feeling.

She pretended to read her book, looking up occasionally to keep her eye on Billy. She was becoming quite excited now, her impatience growing. When she saw him stand up, Peggy was on her feet immediately and followed him out.

by NAN BAXTER

Bluebells

THEY were in the hall when Peggy tapped him on the shoulder. "Hello, Billy," she said, smiling broadly. He turned round, gazed at her without any sign of recognition and with a gasp of horror Peggy realised she was looking into the eyes of a complete stranger.

"I'm so sorry . . ." Peggy was immediately flushed with embarrassment. "I've made such a stupid mistake. You see, I thought . . ." She was stuttering now. "I thought you were someone . . . someone I haven't seen for well over fifty years."

"That's a long time ago." The stranger's brown eyes were amused. "I'm sure your friend has changed quite a bit." He gave her a little bow. "I'm going out to look at the stars," he said, and he was heading for the door.

What must the man think of her? He was the type, she sensed, who would not suffer fools gladly. Possibly, he had already put her down as a silly old woman in her dotage.

She started to climb the stairs to her room and, suddenly, she felt

G

tired. Travelling was quite an event for her these days. She had left Glasgow early, there had been all the excitement of the journey and the thrill of arriving here. Right now, bed was most appealing.

But, cosy though she was, Peggy could not sleep, and she began to let her thoughts drift back into the past. She was a girl again here at Glenbreck in the cottage near the golf course where they had watched the trains go past.

She remembered scene after scene, and people, too. Some of the names she recalled, but others had gone.

When she did fall asleep, it was to the sound of laughter from a group of young people. They must be down by that deep pool on the river. Perhaps she would go there some day soon.

SHE was early for breakfast next morning, but the man she had encountered the previous evening was earlier still. In his tweeds, with a pair of binoculars slung over his shoulder, he was picking up a packed lunch from the hall table and putting it into his haversack before going out.

"The professor is a keen birdwatcher," explained another old lady as Peggy and she went into the dining-room together. "I believe he comes here often."

A professor! Clever folk always made her tongue tied. But she wasn't likely to have the opportunity of conversation again.

Place Of Dreams

THERE is a place where I would dwell,
Time locked within a magic spell,
A place of flowers and grass and trees,
Caressed by gentle murmuring breeze.

This place lives only in my dreams,
To brighten days when no sun gleams,
I hear the bird song, smell the flowers
Enjoy a feast of golden hours,
Someday I'm sure, out of the blue,
I'll find my place of dreams come true.
— Georgina Hall.

She lingered over breakfast, then set off up the main street of the village. There were a couple of new souvenir shops, but the others had changed little. All the lovely tweeds and tartans were there. But it was the butcher's shop that brought back memories. Good red meat, venison, a brace or two of grouse, and jars of heather honey. Was it so long ago since she had last gazed into this window?

She bought a newspaper and went down to a seat by the golf course.

Peggy looked around. The cottage where she and her parents had stayed was closed and seemed deserted. On the hillside behind the village, there were terraces of new houses and the station road was lined with small factory units.

But the eternal mountains were standing out as she remembered them, range after range in all their glorious colours. She breathed in the cool, sweet air. It was good to be back at Glenbreck.

Half an hour later, Peggy set off on a walk round the perimeter of the golf course. But by the time she reached the second tee she was glad to have another seat. Time passed slowly. The hotel did not cater for lunch, so she had a sandwich and a cup of coffee in the baker's shop. And then what?

It was only midday, Peggy realised. She would go back to the hotel and have a good, long read of her book. Later, she might have a stroll along the loch road and by then the time would be approaching for her to change into a dress for dinner.

She had never before had to plan to fill in the hours ahead. It was a dismal experience.

G RADUALLY, over the next few days, Peggy extended the length of her walks and managed to view some of her special places, but she gained little satisfaction. She was lonely, with no-one to share all this scenic beauty. She had come here to chase dreams, only to find a cold reality. How foolish she had been to hope for more.

People came and went. The professor was still there and they exchanged the odd salutation. Once or twice she caught him looking at her questioningly, and she was equally puzzled. This man might not be Billy Wood, but she was still convinced they had met somewhere before. Was he now thinking along the same lines? It was all rather intriguing.

But that did nothing to influence her decision to cut short her holiday. It had all been a ghastly mistake. Never go back, she had been warned, and it had proved right. A visit to one particular spot, the most precious of all, and she would return home, a wiser, more subdued woman. But even there she would face loneliness.

Peter MacDonald's farm was up a rough road from the village. There, in those distant days, Peggy and some of her girlfriends would collect the big brown eggs that tasted better than any others. But the greatest attraction of that road was the discovery that among several clumps of the lovely Scottish bluebells were some that were startlingly white.

Each year they came back hoping these white bells were still there, and they were. It was a fanciful happening that had captured the imagination of the girls. Now, Peggy wondered, could she hope to find them again?

They had always started their search near the rowan tree, she remembered. And here it was, looking more forlorn and gnarled than ever.

And so she began.

Slowly and diligently, she went up and down the road, first on one side then the other. Bluebells were in abundance, dancing lightly in the breeze, but there was no sign of a white one.

But Peggy Martin did not give up readily. She would cover the ground once more and then, if unsuccessful, go back to the hotel and tell them of her decision to leave next day. There was a train at ten.

For a further ten minutes, she searched, but she was out of luck.

She was disappointed, but it was too much to expect after all these years. So, resolutely, she started off, back to the village.

SHE had only gone a few yards when she heard the sound of footsteps, and in a second, the professor was beside her.

"Hello," he said, and they both stopped. "Aren't we lucky to have this lovely weather for our holiday?"

"Yes," she agreed, "it's been wonderful. But I'm going home tomorrow."

"And where's home?" he asked, to her surprise. She would have expected him to exchange a few words of polite conversation and pass on, but he seemed keen to linger.

"Glasgow," she told him.

"That's my home town, too." His smile was warm and friendly and her conception of him as a rather austere man was changing. Now, he was looking at her questioningly.

"Please don't think me too curious, but I couldn't help noticing a minute or two ago that you seemed to be searching for something you've lost. I hope it wasn't anything of value."

She smiled. "No," she assured him, "it's of little importance now, but when I was young it was quite a serious matter."

Briefly, she told of coming to Glenbreck with her parents every September and of how, with her girlfriends, they had found the white bluebells. Rediscovering them every year was one of the highlights of their holiday.

"They were just about here," she indicated. "I've had a thorough look, but they've completely disappeared. Shall we move on now?"

But the professor was standing still and regarding Peggy with amazement.

"I've heard about these white bluebells," he declared confidently. "My sister told me about them. You see, we came here regularly, too, when we were young. Do you remember her — Jessie Carmichael?"

"Jessie? Of course!" Peggy was suddenly glowing with delight. "We're exactly the same age. And you — you must be Adam."

"You're right." Adam Carmichael was smiling happily, too. "I've been trying hard to recall where I'd met you, for I was sure we had met somewhere. Of course, it's perfectly clear now. We were all children together. But I'm sorry, I still can't remember your name."

"I was Peggy Wallace, then," she told him. "But you were one of the older boys," she added teasingly. "It was beneath your dignity to associate with the girls, yet you weren't above chasing us, at times."

He chuckled at that. He was no longer a professor, just a boy in short trousers with a fine turn of speed.

"This is fun," he said. "Yes, I do remember. Now, I think we ought to have one last look for these white bluebells. Another pair of eyes might help."

"That's kind of you." Somehow, with Adam beside her, she felt more hopeful as they started off. They moved slowly and searched thoroughly and all the time they talked. There were so many years to fill in . . . so many memories to dust down and re-live.

Peggy's story was an ordinary one. She had worked in a bank, eventually marrying. Their three daughters were all settled with husbands and families of their own, scattered all over the world. A year ago, her beloved Jim had died and she had moved from her home in a country town to a smaller house in Glasgow. But she did not even hint at her loneliness.

Adam Carmichael's life had been even less eventful. Dedicated to teaching history, he had never married, and neither had his sister, Jessie.

"She was a doctor's secretary for a long time," he explained, "but after our parents grew old she came home to run the house. Jessie and I have come back here quite often. But this year she's got the painter in, and thought it better I should be out of the way. But look — " There was a sudden excitement in his voice. "I don't want to build up your hopes, but I'm almost certain I see something white in that clump of bluebells just to the right of that big stone."

Quickly, Peggy moved closer. "You're right! Three white bluebells! Oh, thank you, Adam."

And, for one exquisite moment, Peggy was a girl again, thrilling to the sight of the flowers.

"I'll go home much happier now," she said.

ADAM was quick to make his proposal.

"I'm heading back on Saturday," he told her. "If you like to stay on until then, Peggy, I could take you home in my car."

How natural it was for them, she noticed with pleasure, to slip into calling one another by their christian names.

"That would just be wonderful," Peggy answered. "I hate travelling on my own."

"Jessie will be glad to see you again," he added.

They had started off, back to the hotel. "You'll be able to pick up the threads again."

How the day had changed! The sun was shining on this September afternoon as it had never shone before. So much and yet so little had happened.

In Peggy's imagination there was something true and faithful in the re-discovery of these white bluebells. Just like finding Adam again, after all those years. That Adam had found the flowers held a special significance.

The past and the future had merged, and the way ahead was clear and welcoming. From this meeting, new avenues of warmth and friendship must surely open up.

"You'll know some of our friends," Adam said, as if he had read her thoughts. "One or two are from the old Glenbreck days."

"And here's another," Peggy added in wonder. Perhaps, at that moment, there was a moistness in her eyes, blurring her vision, so that she stumbled.

But Adam Carmichael's arm was strong. □

ONE STOLEN

WHEN John Steadman first saw her, she was sitting in the window table of a small Spanish hotel on the island of Formentera, and he knew with an unbelievable flash of intuition that she was destined to play an important rôle in his shattered life.

She wasn't really like Rosalind but she reminded him of her strongly. She seemed a paler edition of the woman he had adored for over twenty years, a frailty, a touch of strain compared to his late wife's glowing robustness, and he decided the likeness was more in mannerisms than actual features.

He changed his chair whilst waiting for his dessert, pretending the sun worried him.

Only once did she glance up, giving him a faint smile of acknowledgement to a fellow guest, before returning to the map she was studying. He ate his dinner moodily, wishing for the hundredth time he had disregarded his doctor's advice, and taken a walking holiday in his own country as usual.

The nearness of breakdown had at last forced him to recognise his need of a complete change, yet try as he would, he found it impossible to relax.

His thoughts persisted in dwelling in the past. The happy careless years with Ros, and later the children — Chloe, Clive and Rebecca. They were all married now, and Rebecca had settled on the other side of the world.

They had been such a loving family, so sure of their infallibility to tragedy, but now it seemed the links which had bound them were strained, and often on the rare occasions they were all together, they seemed like strangers.

Sometimes, despite his golf, his music and his chambers in town life seemed totally empty and he was the loneliest man on earth.

WOMEN, attracted by his mature good looks, went out of their way to console him, but with little success. Gradually, he was dropped from social occasions and he retreated more and more into melancholy.

And now on this unspoilt Spanish island with its whispering pines, exotic blossoms and perpetual music, he had seen this woman, and for the first time since the tragedy he felt his pulses quicken and a stir in his empty heart.

DAY

by
GAYE
WILSON

He was sure she had no intention of being elusive, yet she was; being the first comer into breakfast and the last into dinner. He found himself looking forward to seeing what she would be wearing, her clothes were simple but expensive and he recognised the emerald on her right hand as real. In passing her table he would murmur a greeting, which she would acknowledge with an absent smile.

He was sure, too, had she so wished, fellow guests would have included her in their holiday activities for they were a friendly crowd, but he recognised and respected her obvious desire to be alone. He waited with growing impatience for an opportunity to present itself to him when he could possibly embark upon a friendship with her.

He discovered she took a walk along the shore immediately after breakfast. Similarly after dinner in the evenings. During the daytime she seemed to disappear — he couldn't find out where she went. He'd discovered her home address from the hotel register; she was L. Wyndham of what sounded like a village in Cumbria.

ONE evening, walking moodily along the sand, he almost stumbled over her in a rock-strewn hollow where she was curled up.

"I beg your pardon," he exclaimed with genuine concern. "I'm afraid I didn't see you . . . I hope I didn't frighten you."

Her voice was soft, as he had known it had to be. "Not at all," she said, and then added conversationally, "You're staying in the hotel?"

To his delight she chatted easily for a while, permitting him to examine the sketch she was engaged upon and explaining that she was an illustrator of childrens' books. When at last he turned to move on, she delayed him by asking for a cigarette.

Eagerly he offered her his crumpled packet. "Actually, I've given it up," he apologised. "I'm not sure if my lighter works."

It didn't! and she said ruefully "I've given it up, too." And they both laughed. "I should be grateful to your lighter. It strengthens my resolve."

After this, it seemed inevitable that they should stroll back to the hotel together.

"Will you be joining the trip tomorrow?" he asked to delay her a moment longer.

She hesitated. "Is it something special?"

"They all are." He grinned, and named the places where they would visit.

She was interested in a particular church. "Doesn't that one have the golden altar?"

"I believe it has been restored after the Franco war," he said, "but it sounds interesting."

"I . . . I'm not sure," she murmured.

His heart sang as he supplied her with details of the trip and he was disproportionately disappointed when she didn't appear. For him the day was wasted.

A T dinner he was afraid she wasn't going to appear either, and when she did, his gladness faded at the expression on her face. He knew she had been weeping and dare not approach her. There was music in the lounge later, and she sat in a distant corner and never looked up. But the next morning she stopped at his table. "I'm sorry about yesterday," she said. "Did you enjoy the trip? "No. I was too disappointed because you didn't join us." A flush rippled over her features. "I had a fit of the blues," she confessed. "I wouldn't have been good company." "That makes two of us." He tried to keep his voice light. "Won't you tell me your name and share a cup of coffee with me?" "My name is Lindsay," she said. "My friends call me Lynne. I'd like to share a coffee with you to make up for my bad manners yesterday, but first I must make a telephone call. I booked it for eleven o'clock. I'll try not to be long." "Right. I'll snaffle two of the sun beds, and an umbrella." "You may have to fight! There was a hint of teasing in her voice which pleased and relieved him. At last she was beginning to relax in his company, and the realisation of this filled him with unbelievable happiness. "Everything OK?" he asked when she eventually re-appeared. She gave a twisted smile and nodded. They chatted as they drank their coffee, and the sun sparkled the rippling pool with its background of snowy balconies, purple bougainvillea and scarlet hibiscus. "Have you had a swim yet?" She shook her head. "I only like swimming in the sea, and it won't have warmed up yet." "May is early for the Med." he agreed. "It's absolutely freezing." "You've been brave?" "I needed to take punishment." She looked at him dark brows raised. "Punishment?" "Yes." He made a sudden decision to be frank. "Life is too short to grieve for ever." "You've lost your wife!" she cried, and the understanding in her voice tore open the old wound.

▶ p108

CUILLIN HILLS

T HE Cuillin Hills of Skye have long held a mystery and magnetism for sightseers and rock climbers alike.

Some of their peaks (and there are fifteen over 3000 feet high) remained impregnable to climbers until the end of the 19th century.

The Black Cuillins are the main ridge and are so called to differentiate them from the less overpowering Red Cuillins. Visitors should be warned that the Cuillins attract mist suddenly and without warning.

▶ over

THE CUILLIN HILLS, SKYE : J CAMPBELL KERR

"Five years ago. But it seems like yesterday."

Her fingers plucked the edge of the towel. "I . . . know how you are feeling," she said, and a small silence followed which drew them together as words could never have done. Suddenly she sprang up. "Let's have a punishing dip together!"

"Sure," he agreed. "Do you have to retreat upstairs?"

But she was pulling off her cotton skirt, revealing a neat dark swimsuit. Her body was firm, lightly tanned and shapely. Laughingly she twisted her abundant hair on top of her head. "What about you?"

"I'm prepared, too," he said, and together they ran down the sandy steps which led to the beach.

The water was startlingly cold, but it seemed to suit their mood, and afterwards, as they lay in the sun relaxing, they found themselves able to talk freely.

"I wanted to speak to you that first evening," he told her a trifle shame-facedly. "But you didn't even notice me."

"I did," she confessed in a low voice. "I had to will myself not to look up."

"But why?"

"You . . . reminded me of . . . Mark . . ."

"Your husband?"

She nodded. "Not physically. In an unexplainable way." A spasm passed over her face and she changed the subject swiftly. "Tell me about your wife."

"She was knocked down by a drunken driver," he said tersely. "I wanted to murder him. I still do sometimes."

"I understand," she said gently, and he felt the comforting warmth of her sympathy.

FOR the next three nights they sat together on the beach veranda listening to the music and the swish of the sea. They said little, but each felt the comfort of each other's presence.

"There's another trip tomorrow," she said when they parted. "Will you be going?"

He pursed his lips. "Will you?"

"I'd like to." The sadness was back in her eyes. "But I'm half expecting a telephone call . . ."

"Couldn't someone take a message?"

She didn't reply, but he knew she had heard.

"I know!" he said with a whimsical smile, "risk it, and we'll pretend!"

"What should we pretend?"

"That everything's all right with the world. There was no yesterday and there'll be no tomorrow. Let's have a stolen day together with no questions asked and no strings attached."

"A stolen day," she repeated. And her harebell blue eyes in their thick dark lashes lit up. "Where would we go? On the trip?"

"Leave it to me!" His voice was firm and confident. "All you have to do is to appear in reception at say . . . ten o'clock. Dressed for high adventure."

A series of emotions spread over her face, and then she said breathlessly, "I'll be there. Yes, I'll most certainly be there!"

"Promise?"

"Promise."

She kept her word, and his heart leapt at the sight of her. She wore a blue dress of crisp cotton with a floppy beach hat to match. Suddenly, she was young, alive, eager, pulsating with life.

"What on earth?" She cried out in amazement at the yellow beach buggy he had hired for the day.

"Your chariot awaits, madame." He grinned, throwing up the passenger door.

Gaily, she settled herself, pulling off the floppy hat so that her dark hair streamed in the wind like a flag. "Where are we going?"

"To the Never Never Land," he teased, because he felt like a boy again. "Where it is always now."

He noticed how white and even her teeth were when she laughed, and whipped up the speed of the ancient buggy pretending it was out of control.

After about an hour's driving he pulled up beside a rocky cove half concealed by young pines towering amongst clumps of crimson oleanders and pink geraniums which had grown into hedges.

"Could you give me a hand with this?" He was hauling a wicker picnic basket from the rear of the buggy. It was packed with food and wine.

"You think of everything," she said, smiling. "Are you always so competent?"

"I never took a lady out on a stolen day before," he replied seriously.

THEY swam, relaxed, and swam again, and the water inside the cove was luxuriously warm. Afterwards they had lunch — a quite delicious affair of fresh pineapple, cold chicken and salad, sparkling wine followed by strawberries and cream and coffee in a flask.

"I'll never forget this," she said, stretching out on the soft sand.

"Neither will I." He rolled over propping himself up with his elbows so that he could look down into her face. "We can't let it end here, Lynne. I know I'm being precipitate . . . forgive me . . ."

She pulled herself up, putting her hands in a defensive position, "John, you promised . . ."

"I know. I'm sorry. But tell me why it has to be this way? We've lost so much. What is there to stand between us?"

She made patterns in the sand with her bare toes, refusing to look at him. "We were going to pretend. Remember? You promised."

The youthful glow had faded from her face leaving it bleak and drawn. "You promised," she repeated. "It was to be a stolen day with no strings attached. Don't spoil everything."

"Is that what you really want?"

She nodded.

"I find it hard to believe."

"You must." Her eyes were overbright now, and she was biting her lip.

He felt a brute but something drove him on. "Surely you can talk about it Lynne? Couldn't you trust me?"

Her silence drove him mad, and on impulse he leaned across and kissed her. He'd fully expected a repulse, but instead she clung to him with a sort of desperation giving him back kiss for kiss with fierce abandon.

"You feel the same," he whispered incredulously, cradling her head and pressing his lips against her forehead. Lynne . . . darling Lynne, you have to tell me what is troubling you. Whatever it is we can sort it out together."

She sighed. "No we can't." She released herself from his arms. "I should never have allowed myself to get into this position. Now I've hurt you as well as myself. I'm not free, John. I will never be free. It's as simple as that. I . . . I didn't want you to know and . . . and pity me."

"But surely . . ." he was bewildered. "Surely you told me your husband had died?"

"I think . . . I said I had lost him, and so I have. Five years ago. There are more ways than death to lose a loved one. More cruel ways." She shuddered. "I'm one of the massive army of 'carers.' Now do you understand? I can't abandon my husband because of a cruel illness!"

He was chilled, dismayed and horrified. "But how could this happen?"

"It can and it does happen," Lynne said. "It could happen to me, to you, to any of us. It's the price some of us have to pay for growing old."

"But . . . there must be special places, hospitals, professionals. People who cope with this sort of thing." His voice sounded harsh and unreal. "Who is looking after him now — while you are here?"

"He's in a private nursing home," she said dully. "The doctor arranged it. He said I had to have a break."

Looking at her then, he understood the lines of strain about her

▶ *over*

HARDRAW FORCE

CONSIDERED one of the most spectacular in England, this waterfall — Hardraw Force — plunges 100 feet over the rim of Hardraw Scaur into a glen that was once used for brass band contests because of its superb acoustics.

The cliff projects so that you can walk behind the waterfall, and the area is popular with Fell-climbers.

HARDRAW FORCE, N. YORKS : J CAMPBELL KERR

mouth, the ever changing expression in her eyes and her anxiety about the telephone.

"There must be a way out," he urged. "There has to be."

"There's only one way, John, and until then I have to go on caring."

He was silent, trying to steady his rushing thoughts. For the second time in his life, his world had crumbled. "Does he . . . does Mark appreciate what you do? Does he love you?"

"He doesn't even know me!" Her tone was bitter.

"But you've got the rest of your life to live!"

"He's my other half," she replied.

He buried his face in his hands. "Oh, God!" he said. "Oh, dear God! How long?"

"Nobody knows. Least of all the doctor. Nobody can tell."

"It could be a life sentence . . ."

"It might well be, and I have to learn . . . to accept it. I thought I had until . . . Oh, John . . . I've spoilt our stolen day."

"Perhaps . . ." There was a note of desperation in his voice. "Perhaps between us we could work something out."

"No!" She shrank away from him. "We have to forget we ever met — it's the only way."

THEY drove home silently. Even the yellow buggy had lost its lustre.

"Mrs Wyndham!" The hotel Tannoy was paging her as they ascended the geranium bright steps. She went deathly white and clutched his arm. "It's Mark!" she said. "I know it's Mark. I feel so guilty."

He experienced a peculiar thrill of apprehension coupled with a forbidden hope which he battled to suppress.

"I'll hang around . . ." he began.

"No, I'll see you later," she said, and vanished into the office.

Never had time hung so heavily for John Steadman. Three times he walked past the door of her room but lacked the courage to knock.

At last she emerged, dressed for travelling. "It *is* Mark," she said. "The nursing home can't cope. It's happened before, and it's all my fault. I shouldn't have left him." Her voice tailed off.

"I've got a seat on a plane at ten, they've been terribly good here. People are when you're really up against it."

"I hope . . ." he began and stopped. He was not at all sure what he hoped, not daring to acknowledge it even to himself. "I'll come to the airport with you."

"No, please. Don't do that. I don't want unhappy memories. Happy ones are so precious." She reached up and kissed him, but her lips were no longer warm.

Then she was gone, and he stood alone in the foyer helpless and bereft.

"We'll meet again," he shouted silently. "We have to." Surely not even life could be cruel enough to forbid this?

Thrusting his hands into the pockets of his shorts, he walked slowly upstairs to his room, and it was then that his fingers came into contact with the crumpled slip of paper on which he had scibbled her address. Not that he needed it, for the simple wording was engraved on his heart.

He could picture the grey stone house she'd described — High Mist — set on a hill top with the sparkle of the English lakes below. In his vision was a figure dressed in walking attire, anorak, stout boots and a knapsack. The visionary figure was hesitating, peering upwards, straining and hesitating again.

He knew then that some day he would seek out his captive love in her ivory tower; not to effect some dramatic rescue like knights of old, but to offer a different kind of love. A selfless kind which would thrive without possession. A tender offering to succour and support rather than to "carry off" his lady.

Was it possible he could fulfil a rôle such as this, or could it break both their hearts?

He threw himself across his bed and wept. He couldn't remember ever having wept before. When he'd lost Ros his heart had been full of frustration and rage. Now it was full of frustration and pity.

And then, out of the anguish there arose a sprig of hope, like a determination.

Some day . . . □

H

The Grandfather Clock

HE stands in the corner so solid and
old,
He strikes every hour as each
new day unfolds.
He has watched the world pass for the
last hundred years,
He has watched all its fun and its joys
and its tears.

"Times passes," he says, "make the
most of each day,
"For never again will you pass by this
way."
Then he strikes out each hour with a
sonorous boom,
As though he is saying, "Life's passing
too soon."

His warning to us is like Old Father
Time,
But every year makes him more
precious — like wine.
Our grandfather loved him, and his
father, too.
As will our children, and their children,
too.

His faded old face has a charm of its
own,
His pendulum swings with a squeal and
a groan.
He's not failed in his duty through all
the long years,
So, stay with us please for a hundred
more years.

— E. Horscroft.

by
LINDA LEIGH

The Courage Of TIMMY

"WHERE are you going?" Mummy asked.

Timmy knew what to say, he'd been practising all day.

"I'm going to David Howey's," he said. "His daddy's put up a tent in the back garden and we're going to play in it. It's going to be our camp."

Mummy smiled. "Off you go then, but don't be late coming home, and don't go anywhere else without letting me know."

Timmy wished she hadn't said that. He was going to David Howey's but that wasn't the only place. He was going to *the site.*

He wasn't sure exactly what *the site* was, but Kevin had said it was great fun there and he would take Timmy and David, but they hadn't to tell anyone else or he'd give them what for!

David and Timmy were both scared of Kevin. A lot of the boys in the first year juniors were frightened of him, even some of the bigger ones.

One playtime, he'd come up to David and Timmy and asked if they'd anything to eat. Timmy hadn't, but when David refused to part with his Kit-Kat, Kevin had kicked David on the shins, taken the Kit-Kat and threatened he'd kick him in the head if he cried about it or told anyone.

Timmy tried to keep out of Kevin's way, but every now and then Kevin would demand things like pocket money or sweets, and if he

114

wasn't given them he'd get hold of Timmy and kick, nip or punch till he got what he wanted, then promise he'd do much worse things if Timmy or anyone else told on him.

Timmy and David didn't dare say anything.

THAT morning at school Kevin had been quite friendly towards Timmy and David. He'd said they weren't bad kids, and he'd take them to *the site* after tea, but they hadn't to tell anyone. It was a secret place and he didn't share it with everybody.

Timmy had said his mummy wouldn't allow him out if she didn't know where he was going, and that was when Kevin had told him what to say, because David's daddy *had* put up a tent in the back garden, and the boys *were* allowed to play in it.

David's back garden was next to some fields and *the site* was just over the fields, Kevin said. They were to sneak through the back garden hedge into the field, and Kevin would meet them and take them to this wonderful place.

Timmy felt all mixed up inside. He was glad Kevin was being nice to them and inviting them to go somewhere secret and exciting, somehow it made him feel very important, but he was uneasy because it was Kevin they were going with, and he was afraid of Kevin.

He didn't even dare tell Kevin he'd rather not come, and he felt very uncomfortable about letting Mummy think he would be playing at David's.

IT was quite simple to crawl through the hedge and into the fields where Kevin was waiting.

"Told you it would be easy," he said. "Come on, let's hurry!"

Kevin was older than David and Timmy and had much longer legs, and they had to trot to keep up with him.

Timmy liked the fields where there was so much open space. It was warm in the sunshine, everything was sharp and clear and suddenly quieter. The noise of the traffic had become a soft purr in the distance.

There was little to hear except the scrape and swish of their feet on the overgrown path, the bees buzzing in dozens around tall, spiky purple flowers, and bursts of twittering and chirping from the hawthorn hedges, as though the birds were having sudden, lively arguments.

The fields themselves were full of tall stiff grasses with heavy hairy heads nodding in the breeze, and Timmy knew this was barley.

They went round two fields, and at the farthest corner Kevin said, "Through here."

They squeezed through the hedge on to another footpath which had a wall of high boards on one side. The boards seemed to be made of splinters of wood pressed together.

"Look," Kevin said, pointing to where the boards didn't quite join, "We're going in there. That's where they lock their stuff away at night, there's stacks of it, but I know how to get in."

Through the cracks they could see wooden window frames, piles of stones, pipes, rolls of something that looked like foam rubber or polystyrene, a bulldozer with huge wheels, windows, fork lift and dumper trucks, all sorts of things.

"We'll go to the houses first," Kevin said.

Once they got past the compound it was bright and sunny again. They were by some houses still being built and smelling of sawdust.

Further over were the finished houses. Timmy thought they were very nice. They had no garden walls or fences, each house stood in a large patch of lawn, as though in a little field of its own, with pretty flowers and trees around it.

"Come on," Kevin growled, grabbing Timmy's arm and pulling

him along. Timmy had no option but to go with him.

They stopped at a house with all the walls built and a roof on, but with gaps where the doors and windows should be. Planks led from the rough ground up to the front and back doors.

Kevin ran up one plank into the house, across the uncovered joists and down the plank on the other side.

"You try it," he said.

They did, slowly at first. The plank swayed and bounced beneath their feet like a narrow trampoline as they ran up, they kept their balance on the joists, and ran down the plank at the other side, enjoying the feel of it springing under their feet.

They did it again and again, faster and faster, shrieking with delight. Timmy realised he was enjoying it. Kevin was right, the building site was fun.

They stopped for breath.

"Want to do something else?" Kevin asked.

"Yes!" David agreed eagerly.

"What?" Timmy asked, unsure, beginning to feel vaguely uneasy again.

"I'll show you," Kevin said.

THEY followed him to houses where the walls weren't finished. They were surrounded by a tangle of wooden frames, concrete slabs, rusty-looking pipes, scaffolding was clinging to some of the buildings, deep channels were cut in the ground around some of the houses.

There was also an enormous pile of soil with old dead roots threading through it like pieces of string.

Kevin climbed to the top, then sat down and slid to the bottom, dislodging some of the soil.

"Better than the slide in the park!" he said.

David and Timmy tried it, Timmy trying not to think about Mummy's face when she saw his dirty pants and dusty socks and shoes. He knew what Kevin would say if he mentioned it. "Mummy's boy!" he would sneer.

They were having quite a good laugh, sliding down, with more and more soil spilling and spreading around, when there was a yell. "Get out of that, you young de'ils! Just wait till I see your fathers!"

A man with a beard was running towards them. He was very cross. A large dog trotted after him, and following it were three excited, yelping puppies.

"It's the watchman," Kevin said. "Quick, follow me!"

Kevin ran back to the path between the hedge and boards, stopped suddenly and pushed one of them. It gave beneath his hands, at the bottom near the ground, where there was already a hollow.

"In there," he said.

David and Timmy crawled through, which was much easier than it looked. Kevin followed them and pushed the board back into place. "Keep quiet," he whispered.

They held their breath as they heard the watchman go down the path looking for them, and then they heard him going away again.

SUDDENLY, there was a snuffling and yelping, and one of the puppies squirmed in through the hollow and ran towards them. It had bright friendly eyes and big floppy paws. It seemed pleased to see them, and when Timmy picked it up it was soft and warm, and licked everywhere its tongue could reach, his hands, arms and face.

Timmy and David romped around with the puppy, forgetting about Kevin.

Kevin scowled. "We'll have to get that out of the way," he said. "If the watchman hears it, he'll come looking for it and find us."

He picked up the puppy, walked to an old plastic bin, put the puppy inside and closed the lid.

Timmy couldn't believe it. "You can't . . ." he began.

Kevin's eyes had gone hard. "Can't what?" he challenged.

Timmy swallowed. "You can't leave it there."

The puppy was yelping, and Timmy could hear its paws scratching as it tried to dig its way out. Timmy felt sick.

"Let it out." He sobbed.

"No!"

Timmy was frightened of Kevin, but he pushed past him towards the bin. Before he reached it something hit him hard on his back. He stumbled and lost his balance, then heard David shouting, "Look out, Timmy!"

Timmy ran fast, scrambling over the pipes and stones, to get away from Kevin, not really looking where he was going.

LATER, he was never sure whether he hadn't seen the hole, or the ground had given way beneath his feet, but suddenly he was falling. He wasn't hurt when he landed, but it had seemed a long way down.

He looked up. It was as though he was at the bottom of something like a shallow well, but he couldn't look up for long because of the dust and grit falling into his eyes. There was a bumping, banging noise and everything became very dark.

When he looked up again he realised something must have fallen over the hole, because there was only a small bar of light.

He tried to climb up, but couldn't. He shouted for David and Kevin, but there was no answer. They would come soon, he thought. But they didn't. Perhaps they'd gone home because he'd run away and they couldn't find him and thought he was hiding on purpose!

He thought about Mummy and Daddy. Daddy would be home for tea by now. He wanted to be with them. He knew Daddy would be angry because he'd been to the site, and Mummy would be upset because he hadn't told the truth, but he didn't care how cross they were, he just wanted to be safely back home.

He thought he could hear the puppy whimpering again, then

realised he was hearing himself. He was terribly scared.

Then there was a scraping noise. Light flooded back into the hole, making him blink, as whatever was covering it was pushed away.

"It's all right, laddie," a voice said. "I'll soon have you out."

A minute or two later a ladder was pushed down, and the man came and helped him up. It was the watchman.

Timmy was surprised to see it was just as bright and sunny as before. He had been sure it must be getting very late.

"Are you hurt?" the man asked. ▶ *over*

FAMOUS WOMEN

EMMELINE PANKHURST (1858-1928)

Mrs Pankhurst was founder and leader of the suffragette movement. When her husband died she devoted all her energies to the movement and, despairing of success by constitutional methods, founded in 1903 the Women's Social and Political Union, through which in 1905 she and her daughter Christabel started the militant suffrage movement.

During this agitation she was imprisoned eight times for conspiracy and incitement to riot and for other offences, and repeatedly underwent forcible feeding as a "hunger striker."

During the First World War she became strongly patriotic and transformed the WSPU into a national service and anti-pacifist organisation.

Her courage and persistance bore fruit in the enactment of women's suffrage in 1918.

Timmy hardly dared speak, he was sure the watchman was going to tell him off. He shook his head. The watchman's voice became stern.

"Well, you stay there till I cover this hole so no-one else can fall into it, then I want words with you, laddie!"

Timmy couldn't. He started running. The watchman came after him and grabbed him.

"No! No!" Timmy shouted, "Let me go! I've got to get to the puppy, I've got to let it out!"

He managed to twist free and run away again. He felt something cut his leg, but he didn't stop.

The watchman caught him a second time and Timmy screamed and struggled to get free. The watchman was shaking him gently and saying something. Gradually, Timmy realised what he was saying.

"The puppy's out of the bin?" he asked.

"Ay! That was how I found you. I came looking for it and heard it. Then I heard you."

"Please can I see it?" Timmy asked.

"Ay. His mother'll have her back at the hut by now. We'll go there and see them. I'll clean you up and you can tell me what's going on."

THE three puppies lay next to their mother, dozing in the sunshine.

Timmy knew which puppy it was. He was crying again.

"I'm sorry." He sobbed, dropping on his knees beside it. "I tried to stop him, honestly I did! I wouldn't have hurt you! I wouldn't!"

The sleepy puppy wagged its tail and licked him, but Timmy couldn't stop crying.

"Dinna take on so, laddie," the watchman said. "The puppy isn't blaming you. Pull yourself together and tell me what happened while I'm cleaning you up, then I'll take you home."

Timmy told him everything. The watchman didn't interrupt.

"Are you very cross?" Timmy finally asked.

"Not with you," the watchman said, and smiled at Timmy. He had a nice, friendly smile. It didn't seem possible he could be the same angry man who had shouted at them so fiercely before.

"Mummy and Daddy will be," said Timmy. "I'll be told off for coming to the site and for being late home. And for being all dirty and scratched."

"You'll not be very late," said the watchman. "I know it must have seemed for ever to you, but you weren't down that hole very long."

He was thoughtful for a moment. "See that paving stone over Timmy? Try to lift it."

Timmy knew he couldn't, but he tried.

"I can't," he said. "It's too heavy."

"Try to pick up that broken piece instead."

Timmy managed to lift that.

"Think about it, Timmy," said the watchman. "Think about it and then think of Kevin."

Timmy wasn't sure what he was supposed to see, but he tried

to work it out as best he could. He thought hard about Kevin.
"You mean," he said slowly, "that Kevin picks on little boys
because they're easier than big boys?"
"That's exactly what I mean! Kevin picks on you and David
because you're small. Deep down he's a coward, he's frightened to
pick on someone his own size. You just have to stand up to
him — properly — once! You'll never have to do it again."
Timmy thought about it as the watchman walked home with him
through the fields where the barley whispered and rippled in the
wind, past the purple flowers which had so many bees crawling and
buzzing round them they seemed to be humming. After the darkness
of the hole the fields seemed wonderful, even better and wider than
before.

TIMMY knew he'd have to tell his parents where he'd been and
what had happened, and that they wouldn't be very pleased
with him, but what should he do about Kevin? When he
thought about Kevin and the trusting, bewildered puppy, crying and
scratching to try to get out of the bin, a dull, intense anger throbbed
through him. When he remembered his own fright and distress, the
hard knot of anger inside him was even bigger than his fear of Kevin.
The watchman seemed to know when Timmy had made up his
mind.
"Well, what have you decided?" he asked.
"I'll tell Mummy and Daddy everything," Timmy said, "even
though they'll be mad at me, and I'll give Kevin 'what for' if he gets
on at me again, just you see if I don't!"
The watchman smiled. "Next time, I think you really will,
Timmy," he said. "Don't worry too much about your mother and
father. I think I'll make quite a good advocate."
Timmy had no idea what an advocate did, but he was sure the
watchman would try to help him.
"When I tell them how you tried to defy a big bully, and how your
first thought when you got out of that hole was for the wee animal
and not for yourself, I don't think they'll be too cross."
Timmy hoped he was right.
"I'll be needing homes for the puppies soon," the watchman said,
"would you like me to to and persuade your folks to let you have
one? Or, if you canna, to have them bring you to see them
sometimes before they go?'
"Yes! Oh, yes please!" Timmy said.
A puppy of his own would be wonderful. Would Mummy and
Daddy let him have one? He knew exactly which puppy he would
like, and knew the watchman did, too!
"Right, wee man," said the watchman, "I'll see what I can do."
Timmy slipped his hand inside the watchman's, his mind already
full of plans of what he and the puppy would do, if he was allowed to
have it, and together the watchman and "the wee man" went to
Timmy's parents. □

As Young

by
**MARGARET
THORNTON**

As You Feel

"IT was a grand holiday — it was that!" Dad beamed at us all with obvious delight. "I can't remember when I enjoyed myself so much."

I glanced up from Sunday lunch of roast beef and Yorkshire pudding to look at him more closely. He sounded so animated — and that was not a word I would normally have chosen to describe my father. He was a man of few words, unlike my lively, talkative mother, who had died three years before. When she died it was as though a light had gone out — and I still missed her.

"I'm glad you enjoyed it, Dad," I replied. "You're looking the picture of health. Bournemouth must have done you a power of good."

"It wasn't just Bournemouth, lass," said Dad, a ghost of a twinkle lighting up his faded blue eyes, "I've got something to tell you . . ." He hesitated, nervously drumming the handle of his knife on the table.

"Well, come on then, Dad — out with it," said my husband, Steve, smiling encouragingly at him. "Don't keep us in suspense."

Dad glanced round the table at us all — Steve, Lynne and Mark (our teenage children) and me. But it was me that he spoke to . . .

"I met a lady on the coach trip, Janet," he began eagerly. "A lovely person she is, and I've . . . well . . . I've made a friend of her."

There was a split second's silence, then Dad went on, rather more hesitantly. "I know you'll like her . . . She does a lot of sewing and knitting — like your mum did . . . She goes to church, too . . ." His voice petered out.

I couldn't trust myself to speak, but Steve, bless him, answered brightly enough. "Well, good for you, Dad. That's wonderful news. Does she live locally?"

"Yes." Dad nodded. "Just round the other side of the park. She's a widow, about a couple of years younger than me . . . I know you'll like her, Jan."

That was the second time that Dad had said that. Who was he trying to convince, I wondered? Himself or me?

I forced myself to smile feebly at him. "Well, that's great, Dad,"

I said quietly. Now, if you'll excuse me . . . I must get on."

I HURRIED into the kitchen to fetch the apple pie and cream. Steve quickly followed me. His eyes were concerned as he put his arm round me. "What's the matter, Jan? Oh, come on, love, you're not upset at your dad's news, are you? Now, why ever should you be upset?"

"I don't know, Steve," I snapped. "I can't explain. Just leave me alone for a minute. Go and talk to Dad while I dish out this pie."

"All right, love. But try not to worry," Steve said placatingly. "This could be the best thing possible for your father, you know."

A hard slam of the cupboard door made me feel better, and when I returned to the dining-room I had pulled myself together.

"Come on, Dad — have some more apple pie," I said brightly.

Dad smiled at me. "Thanks, Janet. This is grand — just like your mother used to make . . . This girl I've met likes cooking. She makes all those fancy things — quiches, and volo . . . whatever they're called."

"I glanced reprovingly at Lynne and Mark who were trying to stifle their giggles, presumably at their grandad's use of the word "girl."

"Eeh — listen to me," Dad went on. "Girl, I said! But it's a funny thing, you know. They're always girls, no matter how old you are."

"What's your new friend called, Dad?" Steve asked. "You didn't say."

"Er . . . Mrs Oldham. I told you she was a widow, didn't I? She has two married sons." Dad seemed a little ill at ease, looking down at his plate, too, obviously concentrating on his apple pie.

Now what was troubling him, I wondered? I was thankful to retreat to the kitchen. There is something very theraputic about washing-up!

I DIDN'T see my father again until the following Saturday. I was busy all week with my part-time office job and my household chores, but I always saw him at weekends. He rang up on Saturday at lunchtime and asked me to call on the way back from town. Mrs Oldham was coming for tea. He was sure I would like to meet her . . .

Dad came to the door immediately when I knocked. "Come on in, lass. We've been waiting for you, haven't we . . . dear? Now, Janet, this is Mrs Oldham. This is my daughter, Janet." He introduced us with obvious pleasure.

I looked keenly at the lady as we shook hands, though not too searchingly, I hoped. A rather short, plump person, grey hair with an attractive silver rinse, a hand-knitted mauve twin-set and pearls, a tweed skirt covered by . . . no — it couldn't be! I looked again. Yes, it was . . . It was Mum's apron, the yellow one with the pretty lace edging that she'd made from a remnant.

Mrs Oldham noticed my surprised glance, and she gave an embarrassed laugh. "Yes — your dad's got me working already. Pinny on, too. I was just buttering the bread."

I walked towards the living-room at the back of the house.

"No, Jan. We're in here today." Dad led the way into the lounge, or the "front room" as he always called it, seldom used except for special visitors or at Christmas.

Now a welcoming fire blazed in the hearth, and I noticed that the rather shabby easy chairs had been rejuvenated with loose covers in a gay cretonne of pink roses.

"It's very nice to meet you, Mrs Oldham," I said, hoping that I sounded friendly.

"Now, dear, let's not be so formal," that lady answered. "Why don't you call me Betty?"

Betty! No — it wasn't possible . . . That was Mum's name. How dare she be called Betty! I felt the colour rush to my cheeks. I glanced at Dad, who was staring at his feet. No wonder he had acted so strangely when we had asked her name. It was funny — we had never thought to ask her christian name. Not only was she wearing Mum's apron, she now had Mum's name as well.

"Your dad tells me you're going on holiday next week, Janet. You must be looking forward to it?" Betty smiled encouragingly. "Do you like London?"

I tried to answer normally. "Oh yes — we both love London. There's always so much to do there."

"Fred — that was my husband — he died four years ago — he used to take me to London." Betty gave a little laugh. "I used to enjoy it, but I think I'm a bit old for the big city now. I prefer something a bit more restful. Bournemouth was lovely, wasn't it, Bill? All those nice gardens — and the shops."

"Yes, it was grand." Dad joined in now. "We walked for miles, didn't we? Do you remember the day we walked to Christchurch and had tea at that little café . . . ?"

I sat quietly and listened to the holiday reminiscences. Betty was really very nice. Homely and chatty — very much like Mum, in a way. I wondered if that was why Dad had been attracted to her.

I pulled myself back from my wandering thoughts. "It's been nice to meet you . . . Betty. I must dash off now and feed my hungry family. Goodbye, Dad. I'll call before we go away."

"Now, don't you worry about your dad while you're in London," Betty said. "I'll keep an eye on him."

I've no doubt you will, I thought, as I drove away in my red Mini.

BUT Janet, my dear, I can't understand why you're so upset." Aunt Ada looked at me anxiously. "You say your dad's met a lady? Well, jolly good luck to him. She sounds very suitable — so what's the problem?"

Since Mum died I had often turned to her sister, Aunt Ada, for advice. She was always ready to lend a sympathetic ear.

I looked at her despairingly. "Oh, I don't know, Auntie . . . It's all so unfair. Dad never seemed to take any notice of Mum. Now, he's all over this woman. Even new chair covers! He'd hardly spoken to Mum at times. When I think of how she used to run around after him — food on the table when he came home from work, slippers by the fire — and he never appreciated it . . ."

"Now, just listen to me, Janet. Your mum did all that because she loved your dad. And he loved her, too. He may not have been one for fancy words, but he did care. People have different ways of showing affection."

I stared thoughtfully into the fire.

"Come on, Janet love." Aunt Ada spoke a little sharply. "I can see you're a bit upset, but it isn't like you to be unreasonable. You wouldn't begrudge your dad a bit of happiness, would you? He'd never have glanced at another woman while your mum was alive, surely you know that?"

"Of course I do, Auntie," I replied rather grudgingly. "But I just can't understand this romance, or whatever it is. But then I know it sounds silly but I don't really know Dad very well, do I?"

"Oh, he's difficult to get to know, I agree." Aunt Ada nodded. "And I know he never took much notice of you when you were a little girl. He left it all to Betty — I suppose men did in those days — and with you being the only one, it's naturally your mum made such a lot of you."

"And now it's too late." I sighed.

You

YOU are the pattern of my life
And every sign is printed true,
You are the wisdom of the ages
And all things new.
You are my night, my canopy of stars
Gleaming above me as a tender fire,
Filling my heart and mind with dreams
And my being with desire.
And you, you are my daybreak
Bringing the sunrise and the early dew,
All I wish to do, could hope to know
Is within you.
You are my strength and my weakness,
My boundless joy and deepest sorrow,
You are my tears and my laughter,
My yesterday and my tomorrow.

— *Patricia Samuels.*

IT'S never too late, Janet. You try to get a bit closer to your dad — and to Betty, too, and you'll feel a lot happier. So will Bill."

"I'll try, Auntie," I said. "But, they're a bit old, aren't they? Dad's sixty-five — and she's not much less."

"What's that got to do with it?" Aunt Ada raised her eyebrows. "We're still capable of deep feelings, no matter what age we are. I know I'm not married — perhaps you think I don't know what I'm talking about — but I've had my moments . . .

"I wouldn't get married for love nor money now, I'm too fond of my independence. But there's one or two fellows at the club who wouldn't need much encouraging." She gave a quiet chuckle.

"You're a dark horse, Auntie," I said, laughing.

"Yes. It's a funny thing, Janet. I can't believe I'm old. I know my hair's grey, and I'm not as slender as I used to be, but in my mind I feel just the same as I always did. I daresay it's the same with Bill. Just think about it, Janet. How old do *you* feel?"

"I'm nearly forty," I replied. "You know I am."

"I didn't say how old *are* you — I said how old do you *feel?*"

"I don't know. I suppose I feel about twenty-five," I said.

"Well, there you are then. We're all just as young as we feel. I should imagine this friendship has worked wonders for your dad. He's been on his own a lot since your mum died. Now, what about next week? I'm looking forward to having Lynne and Mark while you're away."

We discussed the childrens' forthcoming visit, and when I left I felt much happier.

T HE holiday in London was just the tonic I needed. We even managed to get tickets for a terribly popular musical.

I was unpacking when the phone rang.

I heard Steve answer. "Hello, Aunt Ada . . . Yes, we're back, safe and sound. Oh dear . . . Why didn't you send for us?"

I hurried into the room. "What's the matter, Steve?"

He motioned to me to be quiet. "Oh, I see . . . So there's no danger . . . Yes, of course, we'll be over as soon as possible . . . 'Bye, Aunt Ada."

"Steve, what is it?" My voice was shrill with anxiety.

"Now — sit down, love. It's your dad — he's had a slight heart attack."

I gasped and put my hand to my mouth in horror.

"Steady on, love." Steve put his arm round me. "It was only a slight one, and he's going to be all right. Luckily he was at Betty's when it happened. She acted very promptly and got him straight into hospital."

"But why didn't they send for us?" I felt numb. Dad was ill and I'd been away . . . I should have been there."

"There was no real danger. Your dad's pretty strong, you know. They kept him in overnight, then discharged him — provided there was someone to look after him. He's at Betty's now."

"Well, come on then." I grabbed my coat. "What are we waiting for?"

Dad was sitting by the fire. A plaid rug covered his knees and a cup of tea was on a little table near him. Betty was bustling about in the kitchen, and Dad was obviously enjoying the attention.

"Well this is a fine carry-on, isn't it?" He smiled weakly. "Fancy your old dad having a bad attack."

I went over and kissed him. "I'm glad to see you're being so well looked after. You're goint to be all right, you know, Dad."

"Of course I am. I'll be around for a long time yet." He chuckled. "I've still got a lot of living to do."

I went into the kitchen to talk to Betty. The tears sprang to my eyes as I put my arm round her. "Thank you for all you've done for

Dad," I said. "I feel so guilty — we weren't even here."

"Now, don't start blaming yourself . . . Here — wipe your eyes. Bill won't want to see you upset." Betty handed me a tissue. "We were going to send for you, but your dad wouldn't hear of it. 'Let the lass enjoy her holiday,' he said. Of course, if there had been any real danger, we'd have got in touch with you straightaway. You're his daughter — I can't take your place," she gave a wry smile, "nor your mum's either."

WHAT do you mean, Betty?" I said quietly.

"Oh, I realised that when he was in hosital. One of the nurses remembered your mum. Bill had quite a chat with her when he recovered a bit. He kept telling Ada and me about her last illness — how patient she'd been, and how the nurses had been so fond of her. No, Janet — he'll never forget her — just as I will never forget my Fred . . ."

Betty smiled again, rather sadly. "But life has to go on. We have to look forward, not back, and make the most of the time that's left to us."

"Thank you for making him happy," I said, and I really meant it. "He's been quite different since he met you."

"He needs someone to do most of the talking, doesn't he?" Betty said. "I gather your mum was quite a live-wire, wasn't she? I wish I'd known her."

"She was indeed," I replied. "You're quite a lot like her . . ."

"So I've been told," Betty said. "I know how you must have felt at first, both of us having the same name as well. But I think you and I are going to be good friends." She put her arm round my shoulders. "Your dad can stay here till he's feeling better. I know a few tongues will wag, but let them. You don't care when you get to our age. And after that — we'll just take things as they come . . . We'd better go back in there. The men will wonder what we're doing."

Dad looked up as we came into the living-room. "You've been a long time, you two girls."

"I was thanking Betty for looking after you, Dad." I went and sat on the rug at his feet. "You're quite at home here, aren't you?"

"I'll say I am." Dad placed his hand fondly on my head. "It's not much fun on your own, lass, but I've got a grand family. And I don't think I'll be spending much time on my own from now on." He smiled and reached out his hand to Betty. "What do you say, my dear?"

"No, Bill," Betty said quietly as she held his hand. "I think our lonely days are over . . . Now — what about some tea? You will stay and have a meal with us, won't you?"

"We'd love to," I replied.

I rejoiced in Dad's obvious contentment. I didn't know what the future might hold. As Betty said, we had to take things as they came.

But I knew that it was the start of a new relationship for Dad and me. □

ALL THAT MIGHT HAVE BEEN

by ANNA BRAMWELL

"ME do it," Alice said firmly, pushing away her mother's restraining hand and clutching the measuring jug in her own chubby fist.

"Just a trickle then," Stephanie told her, and Maggie from across the table, efficient in her Postman Pat apron looked up with a frown.

"Don't drown it," she said.

Stephanie hid a smile. She was frequently jolted out of her calm at hearing her own catch phrases issuing out of her six-year-old's mouth — and in exactly the same tone.

Do I sound as bossy as that, she wondered? She still found herself using some of her own mother's words, even after all these years. And so it goes on, she thought, it was rather comforting.

The telephone rang from the hall as she was reaching down the strawberry jam. She groaned, and grabbed a paper towel to clean her fingers.

"Don't touch a thing till I get back," she warned, as she hurried into the hall.

"Yes?" she said shortly into the receiver.

"Sounds as if it's a bad time to call." The voice was amused, if a bit hesitant.

"Roz," she cried, her irritation evaporating. "It's been ages. How are you? I'm just having a cook in with the terrible two. Hang on a sec . . ." she said, as loud shrieks emerged from the kitchen. "Girls," she bellowed, "stop that noise at once. Sorry, Roz, I . . ."

"Look, I won't keep you, Steph. Just wondered if I could dump myself on you this weekend. I'm a bit at a loose end!"

Steph's mind raced. Tomorrow was the village fête. They'd a busy day planned. But Roz's voice held a definite need.

"Of course you can. It'll be lovely. Pete, too?"

"Not Peter." There was a hint of a pause. "He's away. Tell you about it later."

"I should warn you, it's the village fête to —" Her words were drowned by screams of rage as Maggie came bursting into the hall, her face streaked with flour and scarlet with fury.

"Alice's a horrible pig, she won't let go the rolling-pin. I hate that girl, I hate her."

"I'll have to go, Roz," Stephanie sighed, "and sort out the horrors."

"Go easy on them. See you all about seven."

NOW then!" Stephanie plonked down the receiver and turned to her daughter. "Let's see what you've been up to."

Her face dropped at the mess that greeted her. Her feet crunched on crystals of sugar, something she hated — you never managed to brush it all away. Water trickled down from the table on to a fine layer of spilt flour.

Someone had let Bilbo in and he was nosing a jammy spoon in and out of chair legs leaving a trail of floury paw marks.

In the midst of it all, Alice prodded away at a glutinous mass with her little rolling-pin.

"It's a bit difficult." She beamed at them, pushing back a lock of hair with sticky fingers.

In the hustle of cleaning up there was little time to wonder what might have precipitated Roz's call.

It was later in the evening when she went out to the utility room for a dish of lasagne from the deep freeze that she gave it thought.

She surveyed the range of entries for the fête all lined up on the counter top under their protection of cling film.

There were the girls' plates of carefully-selected six jam tarts, her own Victoria sponge and shortbread and the jars of strawberry jam, lemon curd and chutney.

In the sink up to their necks in a pail of water were the wild flowers they'd picked early in the day, a brilliant mass of colour from the blue of the cornflowers, the buttercups and scarlet poppies with wild grasses, ferns and feathery cow parsley.

She'd get the vases out in the morning for the girls to fill for the competition. There'd been no time tonight. She hadn't counted on having to wash their hair. There'd be Bilbo to bath, too. Maggie had insisted he be entered for "the dog with the most appealing face."

Well, she could leave that to Matthew.

MATTHEW'S eyes had taken on that guarded look when he heard that Roz was expected. It wasn't that they didn't get on — they did. They all loved Roz and enjoyed her visits. It was later, after she'd gone that Stephanie would find herself mooching around, moody and unsettled.

She hated herself for it and did her best to hide it. But Matthew always knew.

Was it that in Roz she saw all that she might have achieved herself? Roz with her exciting job, super flat, holidays in exotic places.

Yet it wasn't just envy. Given the choice, she'd never dream of swapping rôles with Roz. Most of the time she'd have said she was happy. It was only occasionally she'd ache for lost opportunity.

They'd had such plans, she and Roz. They'd been friends from the first day at infant school. They even got into the same college revelling in their new-found freedom. It had been such fun and the future bright with possibilities.

And then in the summer of her second year she'd been called home. Her father had been killed in a car accident and her mother seriously injured.

There'd been no question of her going back to college. With Lucy and James barely sixteen, someone had to keep the home going. And later, when her mother was allowed home, she needed endless care.

★   ★   ★   ★

She was down the garden cutting a lettuce from her salad patch when Roz came looking for her.

"Doors and windows wide open, no-one about!" she called. "You wouldn't do that in London. Where's everybody?"

Stephanie dropped the rug she was carrying and hugged her friend.

"Matt's putting the girls to bed. It's so good to see you." She stood back admiringly. In her pink track-suit, her tawny hair crimped and flowing, she was an exotic flower in the soft green surroundings.

"Mm." She flung back her head and inhaled deeply. "Isn't this just paradise? You can't imagine what it was like in town . . . noisy, dirty and solid with traffic. You don't know how lucky you are, Steph."

Stephanie smiled. "Grass is always greener . . ." she murmured, picking up her basket and linking arms. "Help me pick raspberries for supper, then I'll take you to say goodnight to the girls."

As always the girls commandeered Roz for a goodnight story. As Matt and Stephanie pottered between kitchen and dining-room they could hear shrieks of laughter from up above.

Supper was never an elaborate meal and Roz insisted on being treated as family. But the lasagne was bubbling hot and the salad crisp and piquant with herbs from the garden. There was home-made bread and the raspberries they'd picked that evening.

Matthew opened a bottle of redcurrant wine and Roz sipped appreciatively.

"Delicious, Steph, heavenly colour. You entering this?" she leaned across the table in wonder, "whoever would have thought you'd turn out so domesticated?"

"Ough!" Stephanie groaned, "you make me sound like a broody hen."

But Roz had turned her attention to Matt.

"She used to be so brilliant," she told him almost accusingly.

"What makes you think she still isn't?" Matthew's eyebrows gave a humorous twitch as he pushed back his chair to fetch the cheeseboard and dropped a light kiss on his wife's hair.

Stephanie, looking up with a smile, saw that Roz's face had grown bleak, and wondered.

Later, Matthew took himself off down the village, he said to lend a hand with the marquee in the cricket field but Stephanie knew he was being tactful. They knew each other so well after eight years. Though even after their first encounter there'd been a mutual recognition.

SHE'D needed a builder when her mother was allowed home. Someone to fit ramps and other aids to help cope with a wheelchair. The social services recommended Matthew. And for Stephanie, worried and apprehensive, his practical assurance had given her the confidence she needed.

Everyone liked him, this big strong man with the steady gaze and firm capable hands. He kept turning up, even after the work was finished, with new ideas and gadgets to make things easier.

Steph's heart would lift at the sound of his pick-up truck turning into the drive and she'd hurry to meet him.

They were married just before the twins left home for college. Roz who was chief bridesmaid had reacted strongly to the news.

"Now you'll never get away," she moaned. "I can understand you had to postpone your career; but now the twins are off your hands and your poor mother . . ." Her voice tailed away. It was clear to everyone that Jessica was failing.

"Don't say it!" Stephanie commanded. "There are some things

more important than careers. I love Matthew and this is where I want to be."

And her mother had lived to see her roses bloom once more and to hold her first grandchild, Maggie.

★　　★　　★　　★

I ALWAYS think of your mother, when I smell Compassion." Roz breathed in the fragrance from the climbing rose that adorned the wall of the house. "I remember the day she planted it and thinking how its name suited her. She was a lovely lady."

They'd taken their coffee out into the garden and were sprawled out on reclining chairs. Roz's voice was wistful. Her parents were divorced when she was only five and her mother, who owned a boutique in the nearby town, had displayed little understanding or affection to her child. Roz spent as much time as she could round at Steph's home.

They were silent for a while, both occupied with their memories. Then Roz sat up abruptly, hugging her knees.

"You happy, Steph?" she demanded. "With all this." She gestured at the house and garden. "Living in your old home? With Matthew and the girls? What I mean is," she said stumblingly, "is it enough? Don't you sometimes feel stifled? Have regrets?"

Rainfreshed

GREEN boughs hang heavy after
　　stormy rain,
Their leaves enmeshed,
The flowers give forth their perfume
　　once again
And stand refreshed.

The birds' half-muted songs ring out
　　once more
In melody
That hauntingly re-echos at heart's core
In harmony.

Young rabbits frisk amidst the rain-
　　dewed grass
In joy of life,
No thought of strife,
While freshened hours of evening
　　pass.

　　　　　　　— Margaret Comer.

Carefully, she placed her cup on the ground by her chair.

"What brought this up?" she asked gently. "What's it all about, Roz? You and Pete?"

Roz's head was bent, her fingers twisting the strands of hair hiding her face.

"Pete's gone," she said flatly, her voice muffled. "Taken another job, miles away, the other end of the country. He says it's an opportunity not to be missed." There was an underlying hurt in the carelessly-spoken words.

"When was this?"

"Six weeks ago. He comes down weekends or I go up. But it's such a long way, we're flaked out by the time we get there." She took a long shaky breath and Stephanie sensed what was to come.

"Would you believe . . . he's found a house, already? Wants me to join him. Says it's time we thought about starting a family. Doesn't mention my career, all the years I've worked to get where I am. That's secondary. It's what he wants that's important. Oh, Steph!" There were tears in her voice, "I just don't know what to do."

STEPHANIE sprang up and put her arms round the small hunched figure as if it were Maggie or Alice.

"Come on, love," she said comfortingly, "with all your training and experience you'd get something up there. To begin with I mean. And later . . . well lots of women manage to combine a career and family."

"Oh, it's all right for you. You've always been part of a loving family. All that tradition it was bound to rub off. But you know what my home was like. I've nothing to build on."

Stephanie's eyes ranged over the walls of her old house, the ancient fruit trees planted by her own grandparents, the fully-matured shrubs, all familiar, well loved. She realised with a small stab of guilt how much she'd taken it for granted. How easy, because of its very familiarity, it was to undervalue.

She thought of Matt and the children and felt a deep sense of thankfulness. When she turned back to Roz it was as if she drew wisdom from the familiar surroundings.

"Look at it this way," she said, "any tradition has to start somewhere. Perhaps it's up to you and Pete to begin one. Just think," and she gave a gurgle of laughter, "when you're a wrinkled, grey-haired old granny how proud you'll be to look back and say — Pete and me, we started all that!"

Roz sank back in her chair, her eyes on the distant hills.

"I was to have gone up there this weekend," she said, "but we had a row last night when he rang. All he could talk about was the house and I got fed-up and snapped at him. He told me that if that's the way I felt, why bother to come up and I slammed the phone down on him. Oh, Steph . . ." she looked up pleadingly, "I'm so afraid we're breaking up. Tell me what I should do."

Stephanie bent her head and flicked at a gnat.

"What it all comes down to is how you feel about Pete. I always thought you two were just great together. When you think about it, Roz, what are the odds against meeting just the right person? Most people never do. They have to settle for something less or go it alone. Which may be all right for some, but, Roz . . ." and she leaned over and put her hand on her friend's shoulder, "there really is nothing better than sharing your life with someone you love and who feels the same about you."

LATER that night, as she stared dreamily into the darkness, she looked back on the evening. There'd been no chance of further intimacies as Matthew had returned and the talk had become more or less general.

She hoped passionately that Roz was not going to make a mess of things. Pete was too good to lose. For two years he'd hung around wanting to make their relationship permanent. Now she'd have to decide. Sometimes, she thought, on the verge of sleep, we need a sharp jolt to make us appreciate what we've got.

Her dreams that night were of Matthew and the girls — warm loving dreams from which she was loth to awake. But something kept buzzing away at her consciousness. A sound. Not the customary scuttle of little feet, nor Bilbo's urgent scratch on the door.

She squinted through half-open eyes at the window. It was too early for that. The first light of early dawn was silhouetting the branches of the trees. Then she heard a car door slam and sat up. It was the hum of an engine that had disturbed her.

She slid out of bed and padded over to the window, just in time to see Roz at the wheel of her car disappearing down the drive. Her face softened. There'd be no Roz at the fête today, she'd be speeding north.

Her hand caressed the polished oak rail as she descended the stairs, her bare feet avoiding the stairs that creaked. Moments like this when the house was still were to be savoured.

Bilbo had heard though and was at the kitchen door to greet her. As she bent to stroke him she saw the letter on the kitchen table.

Sorry to dash off without so much as a goodbye, Roz's bold handwriting covered the page, *I wanted to make an early start. Shall ring Pete from the motorway. Bless you for straightening me out. Mags and Allie will make gorgeous bridesmaids. Will you be my matron of honour (how grand). Blessings to you all and much love. Roz.*

FROM the garden, a blackbird gave its fluting call and Steph's heart soared with it. It was going to be all right. For all Roz's tough exterior, inside she was still a child crying out for love. And Pete loved her; of that there was no doubt.

And, indirectly, Roz had made her see things in a different light. For she knew now that it wasn't envy of Roz that had unsettled her. It was a force deeper than that, that had been nudging, insisting, ever since she'd been uprooted from her studies nine, nearly ten, years ago.

It was the longing for knowledge, expansion, education. Soon Alice would be joining Maggie in the long pursuit of learning. And it was time for her too to take up her studies once more.

It was Matt, who, ever sensitive to her needs had suggested months ago that she apply to the Open University. At the time she'd shrugged him off irritably, asking where she'd get the time.

But he'd been right, and it was up to her to do something about it.

And later. Who could say? What she did know was that Matt and the girls would always be foremost in her heart and mind. □

R UTH KENDALL stared at her employer, Giles Waterman, in
dismay.

"You mean I'm being moved? That I have to leave The
Hollies?"

The manager of the small hotel smiled at her. "Unfortunately, yes.
I don't want to lose you, Ruth. You're one of the best receptionists
I've had, but the head management think you are the one to relieve
at a hotel where the receptionist has been taken ill. Only temporarily,
I hope. Let me see —" He moved some papers and consulted a letter
on his desk. "It's on the borders of the Lake District. A larger hotel
than this — Grangelands."

"Oh, no!"

Giles Waterman looked at Ruth in alarm. Her face had lost every
vestige of colour, and the fear in her grey eyes made them appear
almost black.

"You know Grangelands?"

"I stayed there once. Please, I don't want to go back."

He spoke gently. "I'm sorry, Ruth, but there isn't anyone else. We
can manage, but Grangelands has to have somebody to help."

"But it was privately owned. Not part of a group."

"Our group took it over the end of last summer. It has all been
redecorated, but they have retained the country atmosphere. Ruth,
do go! If you refuse, it will stand you in bad stead and you are doing
so well . . ."

Ruth looked at him ruefully. It didn't seem she had much choice.
"When do I have to go?"

"Tomorrow. So you can get things organised for the weekend."

Ruth nodded and then went into the hall and made for the stairs.

"Ruth!" Jonathan Bradley, one of the guest, walked across to her.
"I've got tickets for —" Then he saw her strained face, and didn't
finish what he was saying.

"My dear, whatever's wrong? Aren't you well?"

"Sorry, Jonathan, but I can't talk now. I'll see you tonight. I'll be
on duty at the desk."

She left him staring after her, his blue eyes full of conern.

STEP BACK
IN TIME

by MARY SHEPHERD

136

ONCE in her own room she stood for a while, unable to believe what had happened. Then, aware that her head was throbbing, her throat dry, she went into the bathroom, came back with a glass of water and sat in her armchair, by the window.

As though unable to help herself she picked up a thick photograph album, lying on the small table beside her.

As she turned the pages, the past crowded in on her. Her wedding day. Ruth Wayne and Lionel Kendall. Amost three years ago now. A day of magical happiness, followed by a honeymoon filled with love and caring, laughter and growing understanding of each other.

Ruth looked down at the photograph of a long rambling country house. Not too large, built of old grey stone with a tangle of ivy creeping round the windows; front gardens sweeping down to the river's edge; a backcloth of patchwork fields rising to wooded slopes behind.

Grangelands.

They had first seen it when they were on a touring holiday with Ruth's parents, and they had both known it was where they wanted

to be. Where they wanted to start their new life together.

And it had been all they hoped. Lionel had ordered flowers — so many that when she arrived with even more, the proprietress had laughingly produced a multi-coloured vase shaped like a cockerel.

Lionel had called it a monstrosity, but Ruth had filled it with roses and loved it. In spite of Lionel's teasing she had kept it in their room, long after the roses had dropped their petals.

They had found a sheltered inlet and swum in the river, drying off on the flat stones in the warm sunshine. And all the time love had flowed between them like a living thread.

What had happened to all that love? The first six months had been idyllic. Then Lionel had lost his job. They called it redundancy, but at twenty-three, the word, suggesting years of work well rewarded, was inappropriate.

Lionel, fresh from college, had been with them only a year, and what small recompense he received was soon swallowed up.

Ruth's money kept them going, but in the small one-bedroomed flat tempers became frayed.

When Lionel did find employment it was miles away at Coppings, a small new complex in the South. Ruth was hurt and angry that he hadn't talked it over first.

Her father was far from well, and, an only child, she was reluctant to leave her mother to cope alone. Lionel insisted on going, saying he would find a flat, but property was expensive and six months later he was still in a single, furnished room.

There were hurried visits, but not too often, fares were expensive, and when he did come, Ruth had always some time to spend at the hospital.

Then, when her father was finally on the way to recovery, Emma Wayne looked at Ruth's pale face, and spoke gently, but firmly.

"Darling, you've been a wonderful standby over the last few months, but I'm afraid I have been very selfish. I was so worried about your father, I didn't realise the strain it was putting on your marriage. Go down to Coppings, share Lionel's life even if it is in a single room. You'll manage the finances better between you."

"Oh, Mum! I don't know . . ."

"Ruth, you do still love Lionel?"

"Yes, but I'm not sure if he still loves me."

But Ruth, without a word to anyone, had gone to Coppings.

HER mind still cried out against the memory of that visit, and as she heard the clock striking in the hall downstairs, she rose and, replacing the album, got ready for her spell at the desk.

When she finally put the last ledger away and handed over to the night staff, Jonathan Bradley was waiting for her.

Jonathan had been a guest at The Hollies for the last two weeks. Ruth, who had been a very private person since her visit to Coppings, had found herself at ease in his company. They had been to the theatre and, on her day off, a run in the country.

Now, though, as she saw the serious depths of his eyes, the determined set of his lips as they walked through the grounds she felt uneasy.

They came to a halt at a rough, wooden boundary fence. Below them the village, shadowy in the evening twilight, lay still and silent. The last golden tinge of the dying sunset added a glow of colour, but Jonathan was not looking at the scene in front of him, his eyes were on his silent companion.

"Ruth? What is wrong?"

"Nothing, I suppose. I'm being moved tomorrow, to another hotel. Grangelands, near the Lake District."

"I'm sorry about that," he said quietly. "I was hoping for more time. Time to get to know you. You've said so little about yourself, Ruth. About your marriage."

"There's not much to say. I haven't seen Lionel for months. He had to take a job miles away."

"And you aren't going to join him?"

"No! Oh, I don't know! Jonathan, please, I don't want to talk about it."

"But, Ruth, you must know how I feel about you. I would never consciously break up a marriage, but if —" He hesitated.

"Would I be welcome if I came to Grangelands to see you?"

"Oh, Jonathan! I've enjoyed your company, but . . ."

She looked up at him. He was kind, gentle, and she was so lonely, so afraid of the future. When she felt his lips on hers she put her arms around him, drawing him close, but when they drew apart, there was nothing, just the same emptiness that had been in her heart ever since her visit to Coppings.

HER arrival at Grangelands was very different from her last visit. There were no flowers, no smiling welcome at the large, imposing front door.

The hotel mini-bus picked her up at the station and she was put down at a side door. The girl who showed her into a small, but comfortable room at the back of the hotel was friendly and introduced herself as Wendy.

"You must be Ruth. I'm sure you'll like it here, but I can't stay, we're rushed off our feet. I've left a file with most of what you need to know, and there's a kettle and biscuits.

"Sit and browse through it for an hour or so and then I'll fill you in behind the desk."

Ruth made herself some tea and changed into her black skirt and flowered blouse, then forced herself to concentrate on the file, until she could no longer put off the inevitable.

Slowly she walked through the baize door into the hall. It was all there. The graceful wrought-iron staircase; the thick grey carpet; the huge carved chest; and on it, the cockerel vase. But this time she was alone.

But was she? Somehow she felt very close to Lionel, she felt his presence like a tangible thing, as though he was standing there, waiting to put his arms around her, and tease her about the monstrosity of a vase.

She put out a hand and touched the drooping tulips, but in her mind they were roses, damp, fragrant.

"Hideous, isn't it?" Wendy laughed. "Perhaps now you're here I might get time to do the flowers more often. But then, tulips never last long."

Nor do roses, Ruth thought silently.

☆   ☆   ☆   ☆

Somehow, the next week or two drifted past. Ruth told her parents where she was. She knew they were worried about her, that she should make an effort to go home and see them, but somehow the magic of this place had captured her again. She wandered alone over the paths she had walked with Lionel, on one occasion when the sun was holding out a promise of summer warmth, she even swam in the inlet and dried off alone on the warm rocks.

Soon she would go home. Soon . . .

SHE was totally unprepared for the day she looked up from the desk and saw her mother and father standing there. The rush of pleasure that flooded over her when she saw them showed in her face and her father smiled.

"If Mohammed won't come to the mountain —" He laughed. "I presume you can find us old folk a room," he asked.

"One of the best," Ruth assured him as she handed over the key.

"Ruth, I must talk to you," her mother said quietly.

"I'll be free after eight o'clock."

"No, now. Only for a few minutes."

Wendy was passing with an armfull of linen and Ruth called to her.

"Right," Wendy said, tapping her watch. "Five minutes and no more, or you'll get me the sack!"

Ruth and her mother sat on a settee half hidden by potted plants.

"Ruth, Lionel's on his way."

"But, Mum . . ."

"Listen! He's been several times hoping to catch you. Says you won't answer his letters. You can't go on like this, married and not married. You either have to finish it or make a fresh start. I'm not advising either way," she finished slowly, "but you'll have to see Lionel sometime and the sooner the better. Oh, Ruth, if you'd only gone to Coppings when I asked you."

If only I hadn't, Ruth thought.

Ruth had no doubt in her mind that Lionel would be asking for his freedom. Was that why she had been so reluctant to see him, to open his letters, because at least this way she was still his wife?

But her mother was right. She would have to see him.

The arrival of a coachload of visitors put an end to speculation and by the time Lionel walked up to the desk she had schooled herself to meet him. She didn't know that as soon as she looked at him, all the old love was there, in her eyes. That it gave him hope.

When he held out his hands, though, she turned away, making polite conversation, finding the key to his room.

"I'll be free in ten minutes," she told him, as she handed it to him.

The evenings were still chilly. Ruth slipped a jacket over her uniform. She hadn't eaten since lunch, but it didn't seem to matter.

Briefly she looked down on her wedding ring. A symbol of love, of constancy. Or so she had thought.

She held her head high and walked out to meet her husband.

They didn't consciously decide where to go, their steps took them to the inlet, where the late-evening sun was still sending shafts of colour into the still water. The top of the inlet was protected by an old stone wall which straddled the meadows on either side.

R UTH sat with her back to the old wall, but Lionel perched on a stone, so that he could see her face.

"What went wrong, Ruth? Why wouldn't you talk to me on the phone, or answer my letters?"

"I didn't know what to say, and I didn't answer your letters, because I didn't open them."

He leaned towards her.

Easter Sunday

I TOOK a wreath of flowers to church
   this morning
I went to grieve on things that might
   have been,
And there I found the churchyard warm
   with springtime
And daffodils amid a mist of green.

High overhead I heard the lark's voice
   rising
Ripples of silver over a lake of sky,
I felt the very air alive with gladness
   And knew that grief was vain, and
   death a lie.

A blackbird sang upon the hawthorn
   branches
And on the peaceful graves the
   sunshine lay,
In the dark earth all summer's hope
   was waiting —
And I remembered . . . it was
   Easter Day.
          — C. Betty Haworth 89.

"Love, I know I was impatient, I should have understood about you wanting to be with your father, but I needed you . . . I . . ."

"No, Lionel! You didn't need me." Ruth turned to her young husband and suddenly all the hurt that had festered for so long, poured out.

"I came! I came to Coppings. I wanted to tell you that Dad was better, that I could leave him and join you. Help you find a place for us — but the train was late. There was a derailment and I didn't arrive at the station until nearly ten o'clock.

"I took a taxi to Coppings and found your address. The bulb must have gone on the downstairs landing and it was hard to decipher the numbers. Before I could find yours I heard you laughing and looked out of the window. You were crossing the road, coming up the steps, but not alone. There was a girl with you. I saw her in the light from the street lamp. You were holding her arm, looking down at her, laughing. You passed within a yard of me, but you didn't see me. The girl was looking back up at you and you were still laughing.

"You took a key from your pocket and opened the door, and you both went inside. For a few seconds I had the wild hope that it was the girl's room, that you were just seeing her home, but I looked at the number, and it was yours."

Her voice faded, and she looked at him, but Lionel was showing no sign of guilt, no embarrassment. Instead a little smile played round his mouth, a sad smile, like that of a child who has had a dream taken away.

"Oh, Ruth! My darling Ruth! If only you had spoken to us, come up to us."

HE fished in his pocket and brought out a folder of snapshots. Carefully he selected one and passed it to her.

"Is that the girl?"

Even in the dim light she could see that it was. But she was wearing a wedding dress, and the man beside her was laughing.

"The bridegroom is Ralph. Remember — I told you about him when I first went to Coppings? He was a good friend, but for him I might have thrown the towel in.

"It was Kitty you saw me with. She wanted to arrange for some friends Ralph hadn't seen for years to be at the wedding as a surprise, and I was helping her."

"But —"

"Oh yes, I was holding on to her, and we did go into my room. What you would have learned if you had spoken to us is that Kitty, since she was nine years old, has been almost totally deaf. She doesn't hear traffic, so she holds on or keeps close to someone when she crosses a road. And she hears what you say by lip-reading, so she has to see your lips."

"And, although Kitty has mastered her disability wonderfully well, a deaf person can't make telephone calls, so I was doing that for her. I had just written to you, enclosing an invitation to the wedding.

"Ruth couldn't look at her husband. She had been so wrong, so quick to condemn. Then she felt her hands being drawn into his.

"Ruth, we've both made mistakes. I should have been more understanding, and I should have insisted on talking before now. But I was so afraid. At least while you were still my wife I could still hope.

"Perhaps we were both too young for marriage. Perhaps we should have both done a bit more growing up, but we've done that since, love.

"If we can make a fresh start, I'll come back here, find a job so you can be near your parents . . . and then we'll start all over again."

Suddenly he felt his wife's finger on his lips.

"No, Lionel. If you'll give me another chance, I'll come down to Coppings. We'll get a flat and I can work. Things will be all right this time, I know they will."

Their kiss was long and sweet, and they walked back to the hotel with arms entwinded. Emma and Bill Wayne watched them cross the lawn, and smiled. They knew then that their wish for their daughter's marriage to be as happy and lasting as their own was going to come true. □

FAMOUS WOMEN

EDITH LOUISA CAVELL (1865-1915).

Edith Cavell was a British nurse, famous as a popular heroine of World War I. She was born at Swardeston, Norfolk. She entered the nursing profession in 1895, and in 1907 was appointed the first matron of the Berkendael Institute, Brussels (which became a Red Cross hospital in World War I). There she did a great deal to raise the standard of nursing.

After the German occupation of Belgium she became involved in an underground group, formed to help British, French and Belgian soldiers reach the Dutch frontier. The soldiers were sheltered at the Berkendael Hospital, and provided with money and guides obtained by the Belgian, Philippe Baucq.

But in 1915 Edith Cavell was arrested with several others. They were court-martialed and she was sentenced to death after making a full confession.

Despite the efforts of the American and Spanish ministers to secure a reprieve, she was shot, with Baucq, in Brussels on Oct. 12. Her execution, on a charge which did not include espionage, was considered outrageous and damaged Germany's reputation among the non-belligerent countries.

She gained wide fame for her courage and sincerity, summed up in her celebrated statement, "I realise that patriotism is not enough. I must have no hatred or bitterness towards anyone."

143

I'll Always Be

by BEN MATTHEW

RHONA ELLIS drew into the side, hesitating as she came to yet another unsigned crossing in the twisting, narrow lanes. It was the first time she had driven down to see her father's elderly sister, Amy Ellis, and she realised she was hopelessly lost.

It wasn't a long drive, and, thrilled with the novelty of her first, if third-hand, car, Rhona had scorned the usual train journey. Now the small Shropshire village seemed to have disappeared off the map. Aunt Amy, who knew nothing about the change of transport would be getting worried, and Rhona herself was tired and hungry.

Rhona was the first to admit she had everything going for her. A comfortable bed-sitter; a job she liked in an antique shop; a fiancé, already well advanced up the ladder of his chosen career as a business consultant. Why then, she asked herself, did she feel unsettled, as though she wanted to reach out for something — something intangible that wasn't even there?

Her Aunt Amy had never married, but she had a deep understanding of human nature, and Rhona had had a sudden urge for her company. So she

144

had rung Amy, added a couple of days holiday owing to her on to the weekend break and set off.

Realising time was passing she drove on. It was about five minutes later, just as the lane was deteriorating into nothing more than a glorified bridletrack that she saw the cottage.

Set back from the lane, the garden a mass of tangled perennials, almost choking the rose trees struggling to bloom, the cottage was grey-white, the diamond window panes dirty and some of them cracked. But the thick stone walls which had weathered the storms, sturdy chimneys and a heavy timbered door gave out an aura of strength.

As Rhona looked at it, it seemed to change. She saw it pure white against the distant backcloth of hills; she saw the panes sparkling in the sunshine, or frost-patterned in the crisp cold of an early winter morning. She saw the garden, still wild, still a riot of colour, but tended, the flowers free from the crippling weeds.

RHONA stepped from the car, the scent of flowers was heavy on the air, her tiredness forgotten as she went

There...

up the paved path and peered through the windows.

The combined sunlight and thick layer of grime meant she could see little. But that didn't deter her. It was perfect or could be. Surely Philip would see that? Even if they couldn't live here, it was near enough to Stoke for them to travel at weekends, or when they wanted to relax.

K

Rhona walked back down the path. The "FOR SALE" notice, leaning drunkenly on its wooden support, was half buried in the neglected hedge. Rhona stood on tiptoe and parted the straggling privet, until she could make out the name, then turned sharply as a voice demanded to know what she was doing.

Rhona hadn't heard him approach. Tall, almost heavily built, he stood holding the handles of a bicycle, staring down at her resentfully. Rhona felt her hackles rise.

"I should think that's perfectly obvious. I'm looking at the notice board!"

"Well, I can save you the trouble. The cottage is already sold."

"I don't see any indication . . ." For a brief second a hint of a smile appeared, then the scowl was back.

"No, well, they're a bit slow hereabouts." Then, as though the matter was settled, he looked at the car. "You do know you can't get any further along the lane in that . . ."

"Well, I guessed," Rhona said dryly. Then because she needed help and there was little prospect of meeting anyone else, she added, "I'm looking for Hawthorne Lane."

"Oh well, you're not so far out. You should have turned right at the last crossroads. Keep straight on, past two lanes on your left and you'll come to a sign-post. You'll have to reverse out of this track."

Rhona's face fell. It was only a week since she had passed her test, and she was well aware that reversing was not, as yet, her strong point.

She saw the expression on the stranger's face. He didn't mouth the words, *Woman Drivers!* He didn't need to, his eyes did it for him.

"Give me the keys. I'll turn it for you."

How he was going to achieve that in the narrow lane Rhona couldn't guess, but she was determined to hold her own.

"Thank you," she made her voice sweet. "And while you do that I'll just jot the estate agent's telephone number down."

She saw his lips tighten, but he said nothing. Pushing the scrap of paper back in her bag, Rhona watched him drive the small car a few yards round the bend, then turn it into an open field and drive out again. He handed her the keys.

"I suppose you can manage now?"

Rhona bit back a smart retort. If he had told her the field was there . . .

With one last look at the cottage she drove away.

BY the time she reached Hawthorne Lane it was too late to telephone the estate agents, but her aunt listened as she told her about the cottage.

"I'm sure Philip will love it," Rhona added with, Amy suspected, more conviction than she really felt. "It would be lovely being near you as well."

Amy would certainly have loved to have her only niece near her, but Philip Roberts, well, she was not so sure.

"There was this man there, tall, well, large really. Grey eyes and thick dark hair. Rather disagreeable, told me the cottage was sold."

"Sorry, love, can't help you," Amy told her, mentally noting that for someone she objected to, Rhona had supplied a very good description.

"He had an old bike — once been blue by the look of it."

"Oh, you'll mean Lewis Taylor. Was born hereabouts but only came back last year when his parents were ill. Looked after them until they died early this spring. I did hear his fiancée left him — didn't want the old people. So it looks as though he might be settling down round here at long last."

The next morning Rhona drove her aunt to the nearby market town. Her first call was at the estate agent's, only to be told the cottage was really sold. The men were out taking down the board.

Amy and Rhona spent a pleasant morning shopping and routing round the market stalls, then indulged in a nice, fattening lunch.

When her aunt said she would like to go round an art exhibition that was being held in the library, Rhona was quite agreeable.

THE exhibition was a combined effort by several local artists. Rhona left her aunt with some friends she met and wandered round. The sculptures didn't interest her much, but the pottery was quite good and she bought a piece as a present for her mother.

The art section was across the corridor and Rhona left it until last. The quality of the work really impressed her but it was at a small painting near the exit that she stopped, staring, feeling as though something almost uncanny had happened.

The cottage, pristine white against a backcloth of hills; the windows sparkling in reflected sunshine; the garden, colourful, a controlled wilderness of summer flowers.

She was not surprised when Lewis Taylor came up behind her.

"It's just as I imagined," she murmured.

"And how I see it," he answered. "Look!" He took her shoulders and turned her to face him. "I was rude yesterday. I'm sorry — but, well, I was afraid something might happen and I wouldn't get the cottage. You hear so many things about property deals now. I'm sorry if you did really want it."

Rhona shook her head. "No, it wouldn't have worked. It was only a dream."

"Can I make amends for my bad manners by showing you round the cottage some time. I should have done it yesterday, the agents leave a key under a flower pot . But better late than never."

"I've only today," Rhona told him regretfully. "I had a telephone call. I have to go back to Stoke in the morning."

"No time like the present — if you want to see it, of course."

"I'd love to. I'll have a word with my aunt."

Amy was quite agreeable to getting a lift home with one of her friends and there was a gleam of satisfaction in her eye as she watched her niece leave in the company of the tall man.

Outside, Lewis grinned as he halted by his bicycle.

"You could ride on the cross bar," he said.

"No thanks, I think I'll travel in comfort. Could you get your cycle in the boot?"

Lewis could, and did. Rhona tried to keep a straight face as she deliberately drove past the cottage, reversed into the field and drew up outside the small gate with a triumphal flourish.

"Touché." He grinned, and they were both laughing as he held the heavy door open for Rhona to enter.

"Oh, it's perfect," she breathed.

The cottage went well back and the rooms were large and airy.

"Pale apricot walls all through," Rhona said as she looked around. "Soft grey carpets and some special pieces of antique furniture. Now the kitchen, the palest yellow with dark oak — oh, it's like a dream."

Rhona was full of ideas for the spacious bedrooms, and Lewis watched her expressive face and could see the rooms come to life.

Downstairs he put the kettle on and, whilst it was heating, he scrubbed out a large pot. Then, without asking, took two blue beakers from a cardboard box. He produced a french stick, butter and a mound of cheese and they sat on a window seat and munched.

Lewis talked, and Rhona, somehow reluctant to talk about herself, listened. She heard about his travels abroad, about how, gradually he had given up his chosen occupation of architect and concentrated on his paintings.

"Now it's beginning to pay off. The money from my dad's place will help pay for the cottage and the outbuildings will turn into a wonderful studio. I can rent a shop, sell my work and take commissions."

Rhona was reluctant to leave, but finally she stood up.

"Thank you," she said quietly. "Your cottage is lovely, and I'm sure your paintings will sell."

They looked at each other, the tall rugged man and the small, petite girl.

"Rhona." Thee was a sudden urgency in his voice. "Will you help me? Choose the furnishings — plan the colours?"

She looked up at him, unaware of the regret reflected in the depths of her violet eyes.

"I'm sorry, but I won't have the time. Philip, my fiancé, called. We're looking for a flat. I think his telephone call means he has found one, so . . ."

Her voice petered out. For a few brief seconds their eyes met, then his veiled over, hiding his disappontment.

His voice was gentle. "I'm sorry, Rhona. But if ever you change your mind, remember the key will always be there, and so will I."

SOON, all too soon, she was back in Stoke. Philip greeted her warmly.

"I've found a flat, the very place!"

Rhona, who at the least had expected some apology from him for cutting short her holiday, stared at him in astonishment.

"You mean you've taken it? Without asking me?"

"I had to. They're being snapped up like hot cakes. You'll like it. It's perfect for our lifestyle."

Later, as Rhona walked round the modern penthouse flat, as she stepped through the patio doors on to the balcony and listened to the hum of traffic from below; as she thought of all the other flats in the block, she made one last desperate plea.

"Philip, can we have a cottage as well? In the country for

▶ *over*

FAMOUS WOMEN

SARAH BERNHARDT (1844-1923)

This French actress was born in Paris on October 22. For two years, as a teenager, she studied both the classical style of acting and the popular tradition of the boulevard theatres. She made her début at the Comedie Française in 1862, attracting the attention of the most formidable critic, Francisque Sarcey.

After much success in France she appeared at the Gaiety Theatre in London during the summer of 1879, discovering there that she could be successful on foreign soil.

She played in Belgium, Denmark, the United States and Canada, and then went on to conquer Russian audiences and other countries all over the world.

Miss Bernhardt returned to Paris, where the playwright and director, Victorien Sardou, provided her with three parts that were to be her greatest successes — the title rôles of "Fedora" (1882), "Theodora" (1884) and "La Tosca" (1887). It was Sardou who finally shaped the melodramatic Bernhardt style.

Bernard Shaw labelled it "hackneyed and old fashioned," but there were always audiences to enjoy the flute-like tone of the actress's voice and her broad, histrionic movements.

She then opened the Theatre Sarah Bernhardt, where she first performed as Shakespeare's "Hamlet."

In 1905 Miss Bernhardt injured her knee, and ten years later her right leg was amputated; nevertheless she toured the U.S. again in 1917.

Her last engagement was in 1922 and she died in Paris in March 1923.

149

weekends and holidays? I have a bit of money, I can help . . .''

But Philip had come up behind her and circled her in his arms, drawing her close. She heard his laughter, and his voice was like that of a father, reasoning with a spoilt child.

"Darling, our weekends will be here. We'll meet the right people, join in their social life. I'm going up the ladder, my love! Up, up, right to the top! This is only the beginning.''

Rhona didn't answer straightaway. She remembered how she and Philip had met at the wedding of a mutual friend about a year earlier. How charming and how handsome she had thought him.

She recalled how he had taken her out, wooed her, listened to her. Had it all been a sham? Had he only wanted a decorative, pliable partner to walk with him up that ladder?

Even now, as she felt him near her she knew the attraction was still there. That if he had met her half way they could have salvaged something. But the weekend with her aunt had shown her that Philip's values were not her own; the life he was planning was not for her.

She turned to face him, drawing off the solitaire he had placed on her finger only a month before.

"I'm sorry, Philip, but it's no use. I'm not right for this life. I thought it was what I wanted. I do care about you, but this kind of lifestyle would stifle me — there would be no time to breathe, to be myself.''

He pulled her to him, his face suddenly dark and angry.

"Rhona, you don't mean that! You can't walk out on me!''

She freed herself. "I mean it. You will find someone else to climb your ladder with you. Someone as ambitious as yourself. No, you needn't see me home. I feel like a walk.'' She reached up and kissed him lightly on the cheek.

"Goodbye, Philip,'' she said softly. Then she turned, running from the flat without a backward glance.

FOR the next few months Rhona worked long and hard. She knew her employer was pleased with her, trusting her to go to the smaller sales in his place, complementing her over a bargain, and taking it as a matter of course when she boobed.

At first, although she never doubted she had done the right thing, there was a void in her life where Philip had been. Gradually though, she learned to live ·without him, and now her thoughts turned to a tall, rugged man with curly hair and deep grey eyes.

As the nights grew shorter, she looked out of her bed-sitter on to a sea of lights and neon signs and her thoughts turned to an isolated cottage. were the small diamond windows bright with lights from within? Was there smoke from the wood fire pouring out of the sturdy chimney-pots? What had Lewis said.

"The key will always be there and so will I.''

☆ ☆ ☆ ☆

It was a crisp October day when Rhona drew up outside the cottage. The cottage was pristine white, the garden ablaze with chrysanthemums and Michaelmas-daisies. Inside, the walls were pale apricot, but the furniture was any way. An old table, comfy armchairs and a smouldering fire in the grate, so Lewis couldn't be far. Rhona poked the fire into a blaze and threw on another log. Then she curled up in a chair and waited.

It was about half an hour later, when Lewis, clutching a carrier of shopping, walked in. Suddenly uncertain, Rhona stood up.

"I let myself in. Was it all right?"

There was no need for a reply. Lewis's face registered his delight. He dropped the shopping on the table and took her hands.

"It is," he told her. She looked round. "You've made a start . . ."

"Yes I remembered apricot walls. Then — "

"Then?" she queried.

"We just waited. The cottage and I."

"You knew I would come?"

Suddenly he was serious. "I hoped you would come. I wanted to come and find you, but I couldn't poach on another man's territory, and I didn't know how you felt. I've thought about you so much, Rhona."

She watched his slow smile as he turned to the table.

"Hungry?" he asked. "I am?"

"Let me guess." She laughed. French bread and cheese. Don't you eat anything else?"

"Oh yes, sometimes. But I like french bread and cheese."

She watched as he filled the kettle and cut chunks of bread.

"We have to talk," she said quietly.

He touched her hair with a gentle caress. "Later," he said. "There's plenty of time."

A lifetime, Rhona thought. With Lewis there would always be time.

She bit into the crispy bread. Nothing had ever tasted better. □

by MARY LEDGWAY

FLIGHT OF FANCY

IT was an early-June day. Summer, which seemed to have been
hovering for weeks, had finally arrived. I paused in my prepar-
ations for the evening meal, rested my arms on the sink surround
and looked out of the window.

Charles, my husband, was away on business and I was vaguely
troubled. There was no valid reason that I could put my finger on
— only a feeling of unease as I remembered the letter tucked behind
the clock in the living-room.

I smiled as I heard my younger daughter and her boyfriend teasing
each other unmercifully as they struggled to put up the long, disused
hammock. Harry Oldham was nineteen, and obviously very interested
in the girl who was insisting the hammock was too high.

Sue was seventeen and a bit. Not strictly pretty, but with long, fair
hair and an almost-permanent look of animation, that gave her an
appeal mere prettiness would not have done. Sue, although young,
had a great deal of commonsense, and determination when it was
something she cared about. No, I had no worries about Sue.

Grace, my elder daughter, was different. Twenty-one, gentle, shy
and so easily hurt. Grace was sitting on one end of the padded swing
seat, while Grant Winston sat at the other. They were talking quietly.
Grace's profile, as she turned towards Grant, showed her perfect
bone formation, her hair, darker than Sue's, was cut short and fell in
a shining cap, stirred only slightly by the soft breeze.

This thing between Grant and Grace was so new, yet instinct told
me it was the beginning of something deep and special for Grace.

Grace worked in the local infants' school. She loved her small
charges, and until now had hardly shown any interest in boyfriends.
If anything came between her and Grant . . .

TURNING away, I put the casserole in the oven, stirred cream
into the rice pudding, sprinkled cinnamon on to the stewed
apple, and, duty done, picked up the kettle to make a cup of tea, but
put it down.

I walked into the sitting-room and did something completely

152

uncharacteristic. I poured myself a large sherry, before taking the letter from behind the clock and relaxing in my favourite chair.

I took a long sip and studied the envelope.

Mrs and Mrs Charles Simpson, 28 Gable Road,
Little Haswell, Nr. Grantley, N. Yorks., England.

FOR a while I drifted into the past. Charles and I had met Isabella and Alfonso Sanchez, a young Spanish couple, when we were all four on our honeymoon. We had both chosen a quiet Spanish resort and the four of us spent hours relaxing on the beach, swimming in the hotel pool and searching out friendly little tavernas for meals. When we parted it was with promises to keep in touch and meet again.

The first we had kept, the second had come unstuck. Isabella was terrified of flying; we found a log hut in Scotland that met all our holiday needs, so it was our letters that kept the friendship alive.

Isabella heard about the birth of Grace and Susan. Her daughter, Pakita, was born in between the two dates and we compared notes as they all grew up.

Charles and I wrote sympathetic letters when Alfonso died during Pakita's teenage years. Isabella got a passport and said she would come to see us, but she couldn't bring herself to fly, and hated the thought of the sea crossing. She had carried on the small family business and kept on writing. But now . . .

I took the letter out of the envelope.

Dear Charles and Helen,

I am writing to ask you to do me a help.

My Pakita has had an affair. Not a good one and I have stopped it, but she wants to come to England. She is angry with me, but he was not a nice boy, and I think I was right. I think if she stays with you she will soon be better. Your girls will help and she will meet other boys, more nice ones . . .

I remembered the snapshots of Pakita. Long, black hair, beautiful dark eyes. There had been other boys Isabella had mentioned. And again I thought of Grace, but I could not refuse, Isabella was my friend.

As it happened, the day Pakita was arriving I had to go to the airport to take Charles, who was flying to Belgium on business. School was over for the holidays, and Sue, awaiting exam results, went with me. We waved Charles off then hung about waiting for Pakita.

We recognised her at once.

"Gosh!" Sue exclaimed, "she's smashing!"

She was, and when Harry called round later he obviously agreed.

"Hey, watch it!" Sue warned, and the two of them laughed together.

Sue would cope.

Grant had had to go to Whitby for the day, and Grace had gone with him. They came in about nine o'clock. Pakita was obviously impressed by Grant's quiet good looks, but Grace smiled as she kissed her and wished her a lovely holiday.

Then, her eyes full of happiness, she opened a jeweller's box and lifted out a necklace of glittering, black Whitby jet. We all admired it as she held it against the pale green of her linen dress, but when Pakita picked it up and held it against her dark, creamy skin, the stones appeared to spring to life.

It was Grant who gently removed them from her grasp and returned them to their box.

THE next few days drifted by. Grace and Sue took Pakita round and about. She was quiet, no trouble, but I still had the feeling that all was not well.

Then on the Wednesday, Pakita announced her intention of going to Grantley, our nearest town. When she turned down any suggestion of one of us going with her there was nothing I could do. She was not a prisoner, and had a right to go where she pleased.

Actually, she returned home earlier than I expected and there were few signs of the shopping she had intended doing. There was also a hint of, could it be tears, behind the dark eyes.

That evening Grant came round, and I noticed the way Pakita turned from him, and how carefully his eyes followed her. Later from my bedroom window I saw them in the garden. Grand had his hands on Pakita's shoulders and was talking quietly, earnestly, but Pakita pulled away and came inside.

This time, I did see the hurt on Grace's expressive features, and the wistful look in her eyes as Grant left.

The next morning Pakita said she would visit Scarwell Castle, a local place of interest, but we hadn't to worry, she would be fine on her own.

I spoke up. "Scarwell Castle! Well they say the locals always ignore their own local history. Do you fancy going, Sue, or you, Grace?"

"Well, Grant has some things to do on Saturday, so I'll go. I can take some photographs for the children."

"Might as well make it a proper family outing," Sue said. "No room for Harry in the car?"

Love Is Everything

LOVE is the caring
Through daily life;
Love is the pairing
Of man and wife;
Love transcends anger, pain and fears,
Love is a comfort for falling tears;
Love asks no questions, or reasons why,
Love gives out warmth, like the sun on high.

Love is the bearing
Of joy and sorrow,
Love is the sharing
Of each tomorrow;
Love is strength that eases the way,
Love is laughter for every day;
Love is giving someone pleasure,
Love is an ever-lasting treasure.
— *Gillian Riddle.*

"Not in my Mini." I laughed. "It will have to be a hen party."

I ignored Pakita's scowl. The day out was obviously not going according to plan.

THAT night Grace told Grant about the trip.

"It was Pakita's idea, but we decided to go as well."

I sensed, rather than saw, his sudden attention.

"Pakita's idea," he murmured. "You know, Grace, I haven't been to Scarwell Castle either. I think I'll come along. I can take you in my car, Pakita as well."

I saw the wary look in Grace's eyes, but I could also have sworn Pakita looked annoyed.

Only Sue appeared unperturbed. "Good! There'll be room for Harry. Not that we will see much of him," she added. "He'll

155

probably spend all day looking at guns and armour."

SHE was right. Once inside the castle, Harry quickly disappeared. We made our way up the beautiful, curved staircase to the art gallery. I had fully intended keeping near Pakita, but Grant proved very knowledgeable about the paintings, and as it was a favourite subject of mine, we spent longer than we intended discussing them.

Suddenly, I realised we were on our own. The three girls had disappeared. I was concerned, Pakita was my responsibility.

Grant grabbed my arm and hurried me towards the staircase. We looked over, and there they were. Grace, the black jet like a banner round her neck, Sue, thoughtful as she stood watching passers-by, and Pakita, her long, dark hair a perfect frame for her lovely, oval features, standing behind them.

I heard Grant give a sigh of relief, but even as we watched, Pakita moved. Slowly, then with quick steps through a side door and out of sight.

Sue and Grace looked up as Grant called her name and tried to hurry down the staircase, but by the time he and I made our way down, the hall was almost deserted except for Grace and Sue.

I saw the misery on Grace's face as Grant pushed open the side door, again calling Pakita's name. But it was no use, and he turned back to us with a rueful grin.

"Well, so much for my good resolutions. I'll never make a private eye, that's for sure."

"Grant," I said severely. "What's going on?"

"Look, there are tearooms in the old stables. Let's go and sit down and I'll tell you."

WELL," he said, once we were served. "I knew Pakita had come to England because of an unsuitable boyfriend. You told us that. But what you don't know is that he followed her here. I saw them last Wednesday in the park. Pakita begged me not to tell you, and I said I wouldn't if she promised not to see him again without your knowledge. She promised, but that evening she told me I was being unfair — that Miguel was a decent boy. Funnily enough, I thought the same."

"But why didn't you tell us?" I asked testily. "Then I would have known what to do."

He shrugged. "Well, I *did* promise Pakita, and besides, I didn't want to seem to interfere. After all —" his hand covered Grace's as it lay on the table "— I'm not part of the family. Not yet, anyway."

I saw the look that passed between Grant and Grace, and any fears I had for them subsided. But what to do about Pakita.

I poured myself another much-needed cup of tea, knowing I couldn't leave without Pakita. Then, suddenly, she was there, holding the hand of a young Spanish boy, with an interesting, rather than handsome face, and an honest, straightforward look in his near-black eyes. They both seemed terribly nervous.

"Auntie Helen, I am so sorry." Pakita looked at me rather fearfully. "I did not mean to go, as you say, behind the back. But my mother is wrong. Miguel is not a bad boy. Someone tell her he is but they make mistake. We have to be together — we want to marry

▶ *over*

FAMOUS WOMEN

CLEOPATRA
QUEEN OF EGYPT (69 BC)

Liz Taylor in the title rôle of the film.

The only human being, besides Hannibal, to strike fear into the Roman Empire.

Coin portraits of her show a countenance alive rather than beautiful.

"Her voice," says Plutarch the ancient philosopher, "was like an instrument of many strings."

Cleopatra knew she had to be on good terms with Rome and she set out to captivate Caesar and was said to have borne his child. On his death, Antony became the great love of her life, and then she set sights on her conqueror, Octavian.

His rebuff caused her to kill herself.

A famous historian said, "She captivated the two greatest Romans of her day, and because of the third, she destroyed herself."

A selection of Cleopatras.

. . . Please, Auntie Helen, let me see him while I am here with you."

I looked round the little group. It was obvious that all the young people were on Pakita's side — but what about my duty to Isabella? She had trusted me to look after her daughter, and here she was with the very boy her mother had sent her away to escape from.

I sighed, then made a decision.

"Sue! Go and round Harry up. Quickly. Grant, there is room for Miguel in your car. We'll talk this out at home."

I was unprepared for Pakita's burst of emotion as she threw her arms round me and hugged me.

"Thank you — oh, thank you so very much."

I looked into her shining eyes, and only then did I realise how unhappy she had been. I felt a surge of guilt. I had been so busy trying to guard the happiness of my own daughters, I hadn't taken the time to really consider how Pakita felt. I returned her hug.

"It will be all right, love, really it will," I whispered.

THE more I saw of Miguel the more I liked him. His English was not as good as Pakita's but he made himself understood as he outlined his plans for the future, and I became more and more convinced that Pakita would be safe in his care. But Isabella? I felt I had had enough emotion for one day. Tomorrow I would write or ring her.

But the day was not over. It was nearly nine o'clock when a taxi drew up outside.

"Charles!" I rushed into his arms. I always missed him when he was away, but this time I had really needed him."I didn't expect you for another couple of days."

"No, well. I got finished sooner than I thought. But see who I found at the airport. Asking how to get here!"

I stared at the small, dumpy figure. But, although the slim girl who had shared our honeymoon happiness had disappeared, there was no mistaking the face.

"Isabella!" Then we were holding each other, both trying to talk at once.

Isabella won. "My friend, I had to come. I had the passport and I had no time for the fright. I was wrong! It was another Miguel my friend had the know of. The one my Pakita like is a good man. I must tell her . . ."

I laughed. "Isabella. Please, come in. You can tell her —"

But suddenly the small drive was crowded with people — Pakita hugging her mother. Sue and Grace, welcoming their father. Miguel beaming all over his face, and Grant and Harry struggling with Isabella's luggage.

Over their heads my eyes met Charles's. Later, in the cosy privacy of our bedroom we would, as we always did, talk over the day's happenings.

Life was good, if you gave it a chance. ☐

THE old schoolroom was warm with the heat of a summer afternoon. Sunlight slanted across the twelve children as they worked with varying degrees of industry at the complexities of "What I want to be when I grow up."

The big windows were open and the scent of flowers and the sound of birdsong drifted with the chalk dust in the gently-moving air.

This, thought Jessie Lennox, drowsing on her high stool, is what teaching should be like all the time. Peace and quiet, just half an hour to go till bell time, no tantrums, no struggling to get their attention, no wet raincoats and scattered wellies in the cloakroom.

At times like this, she thought, I almost like the little horrors.

She hid a smile. She was exaggerating, of course. They were good

SECOND CHANCE

by
CAREY FLETCHER

kids, so long as she kept them under control.

But it was rather disconcerting to realise that she had taught some of their parents as well.

She walked to one of the windows and looked out. Beyond the playground the narrow cobbled lane twisted downhill between stone dykes to the tumble of red roofs and white walls of the village.

On the far side of the road three horses swished their tails in the shade of a chestnut tree. Nothing else moved, nothing except a single figure, a man walking slowly up the hill.

Jessie bent to look at Napoleon and Josephine, the hamsters, then frowned. She peered out the window again, studying the distant figure.

There was something about the way he walked . . .

She found herself gripping the windowsill tightly, holding her breath, straining to see him more clearly. Could it be? After all these years?

The man paused and turned to look back down at the village.

Don't stop now! Jessie thought. Don't go back now!

The man turned and walked on up the hill. He was tall, dark hair going grey, clean-shaven; he walked lightly, long-legged, with an easy swing to him.

Just like Bob . . .

He vanished behind the high stretch of wall at the school gate and did not reappear. She waited another minute then, unable to contain herself, went to the door.

"I'm going out for a moment, but I'll be just outside, so no talking."

She hurried out into the playground and crossed to the wall. The road was much lower on the other side. She edged forward and craned her neck to peek tentatively over — and found herself looking right down on the man's upturned face.

JESSIE!" His face split into a broad smile. "Jessie, is it really you?" She nodded and swallowed. "Hello, Bob." This was not what she had intended. "I saw you from the window. I mean, I wasn't sure if it was you. I had to come out and look."

"You look marvellous, Jessie. The years have been good to you."

She felt her face flush. It was a long time — a very long time — since anyone had paid her such a compliment.

"You're bending the truth a bit, Bob," she said. "But I must say you've weathered rather well yourself. In fact, if anything, you've improved."

He laughed easily. "Flatterer. I wanted so much to see you again, but it was a sort of forlorn hope, expecting to find you still here, still teaching. I thought I might have to do some detective work, ask around, see if anyone could remember you."

Jessie shrugged. "I'm still here. Same school. Same classroom, even." She looked round and several small faces ducked out of sight at the classroom windows. "Which reminds me that I have twelve

small hooligans taking advantage of my absence. I must go."
"I'll wait for you," Bob said. "At the gate. If I may."
Jessie hesitated. It would be rude to refuse. Besides, she was
curious to know what had happened to him during the past twenty-
five years.
"All right. About half an hour."
Inside, the twelve small heads were bowed with elaborate intensity
over their jotters. Jessie said nothing. She sat on her stool and
thought back a quarter of a century to the days when she and Bob
had lived for each other, when they had spent every possible moment
together, when she had thrilled to the touch of his hand on her
cheek, the delicious warmth of his mouth on hers . . .
The bell rang a few minutes later.

B OB was waiting for her at the gate. "Carry your books, miss,
please, miss?" he said, mimicking a childish treble.
"Thank you, Saunders," Jessie laughed. "Don't drop them."
There was a silence which he broke just before it became awkward.
"Are you still living in the old house?"
"No," Jessie said. "I've a cottage down beside the river. I've been
there for about ten years now. Remember the Dirty Doolleys? Their
house."
Bob grinned. "I remember. Runny noses and raggy jerseys. And
that was just the parents. What happened to them?"
Jessie smiled proudly. "I taught the children," she said. "One of
them is now a very successful hotel chef, and the rest are doing well,
too. But what about you? I know you became a pilot, but I don't
know much else."
"I became a pilot and I'm still a pilot," Bob said. "The RAF, then
civil aviation. This time last week I was flying a Jumbo into Hong
Kong."
"And why are you here?"
"Just visiting," he said casually. "I had a few days leave, so I've
been touring around in the car. I've an old friend who runs a small
air photography company a few miles from here, and it seemed a
good opportunity to look him up. Then, while I was in the neighbourhood, I thought I'd come and see what had happened to the
village. And you."
They turned down the steep steps between the church and the
library. It was cool here, the overhanging trees in the churchyard
making a green roof through which the sun cast moving patterns of
light on the ancient stones.
"This hasn't changed much," Bob said, grinning. "Remember?"
"I remember," Jessie admitted, embarrassed. This was where they
had kissed for the first time, in a dark corner where the path bent, on
the way home from a dance.
"Nothing's changed much," Bob said reflectively. "I've spent the
afternoon wandering around and the village is pretty much the way it
used to be. A few new houses, a few old buildings demolished or

L   161 tarted up, but . . . well, so many memories . . ."

I have those memories every day, Jessie thought. I'm always here.

"Have you just stopped by in the passing?" she asked.

"More or less," Bob said. "I've taken a room at the Inn for the night. I'd like to look around the neighbourhood, perhaps meet some old friends if they're still here."

THEY crossed the road at the foot of the steps and followed the narrow lane beside the river. "That's my house," Jessie said, pointing to the white-washed cottage.

They stopped at the gate. "I always have a cup of tea when I get back from school." Jessie said. "Join me?"

"Thank you."

She made tea and put out scones and biscuits and they sat in the back garden in the shade of the old hawthorn tree. Somehow, here in the security of her own property, Jessie felt more relaxed and self-confident.

"Tell me about yourself, Bob. What have you done since you left the village?"

He smiled. "Flown several million miles," he said. "Worked my way up from fighters to Jumbos. Been bored and lonely in ten thousand hotel rooms all over the world."

"Oh, but there must be more to it than that," Jessie protested. "Home, wife, family, that kind of thing."

"I have a flat in London," he said. "No wife, no family."

Jessie tried to hide her surprise but failed.

"Does that seem odd?" he asked.

"Well, yes," she said. "You were always a very attractive man; I can't think why you never married. There must have been lots of gorgeous air stewardesses angling for a dashing young pilot."

He suppressed a smile. "There were one or two. The trick lies in slipping off the hook just before you're in the net. What about you? I notice you're not wearing a ring."

"It's a small village," Jessie said lightly. "The supply of eligible bachelors is not exactly limitless."

She knew her answer was a little wide of the truth and suspected he was hiding something, too. She knew why she had never married — it was because she had never, ever, wanted to marry anyone but Bob Saunders, and when that had gone wrong she had retreated into her shell. With the passing of the years she had learned to be quite content to immerse herself in the business of teaching in a small village school.

But she wondered what Bob's reasons really were.

A BLACK and white cat appeared suddenly through the hedge and trotted across the grass.

"This is Minstrel," Jessie said. "She'll be looking for her dinner."

Bob offered the cat his hand to sniff, then scooped her up and

162

settled her in his lap. "She's beautiful." He stroked the sleek coat and Minstrel purred. "Am I keeping you from your food, Minstrel? I'm probably also keeping your mistress from her labours."

"Not at all," Jessie said, feeling a pang of disappointment as he rose and handed her the cat.

"However," he added, "perhaps you might like to come and have dinner with me at the Inn. I'm told the food is surprisingly good for a small village."

"So I've heard," Jessie said. "But I'm not sure . . ."

"Please," he said. "I'll pick you up in the car. Seven-thirty?"

Jessie managed a nod. "Thank you."

When he had gone she sat for a time in the garden thinking of her reaction. Her reluctance to accept a simple invitation to dinner seemed to encapsulate her attitude to life, her careful avoidance of anything new, anything different, anything unknown. Twenty-five years before . . .

She rose abruptly and went inside.

H E arrived at her door at half past seven precisely, looking elegant in a dark suit and white shirt, complimented her on her dress, helped her into the car. It was as if everything he did and said

▶ *over*

The Rose

CRIMSON rich, she shyly lifts
 Her fragrant face to mine —
And all her velvet petals pledge
 A timeless ageless sign.
For, sprayed by early-morning rain,
 Caressed by summer's air,
And sun-kissed under mellow skies,
 I saw her standing there.
Then, wordlessly, you stretched to where
 The rose bush proudly stands,
And now — within a single flower —
 Your love here in my hands . . .
 — *Sylvia Mountain.*

was calculated to put her at her ease, and she responded by forgetting her doubts.

They were shown to a table in a bay window looking down over the river towards the rolling farmlands.

"Remember?" he asked.

"Of course," Jessie said. They had dined here once before, long ago. "Did you ask for this table?"

"It was offered. I accepted. Did I make a mistake?"

Jessie shook her head and smiled sadly. "It was a long time ago."

"I still have the ring," Bob said. "Somewhere. I couldn't bring myself to go back to the shop and say, 'My proposal was turned down so can I have my money back, please.'"

"I'm sorry," Jessie said. "I didn't mean to hurt you . . ."

"It was my own fault," Bob said. "I was in too much of a rush."

"I . . ."

"What?"

"Nothing," Jessie said sadly. She looked down at the tablecloth, remembering with total clarity how she had felt that evening twenty-five years before. She had been in love with Bob, she had dreamed for years of that magic moment when he would propose to her.

And when he did she had drawn back, suddenly frightened, suddenly unwilling — to take this gigantic step into the unknown.

And after he had walked her home in silence and left her at the gate she had wanted to run after him and tell him she had made a mistake and had changed her mind and would marry him, but she never did and she had regretted it ever since.

She had waited, hoping he would give her a second chance, that he would call for her and they would sort things out, but the days passed and then she discovered he had left the village to join the RAF.

THE waiter came and they ordered. The menu was simple, the food delicious. While they ate, Bob told her stories of his flying career, amusing stories for the most part but sometimes frightening, of storms and lightning and engine failures.

By the end of the meal they were relaxed with each other, all awkwardness forgotten, as if the intervening twenty-five years had never happened. When they left the hotel he suggested they walk back to her house and she agreed readily.

They walked in easy silence for a while, then Bob said, "Did you never, ever, want to see what the big world is like? Did you never fancy leaving the village, even for a little while?"

"Never," Jessie admitted. "You know what I'm like, Bob. Unwilling to risk anything new, anything different. I'm too reserved, too inhibited."

They walked on. All too quickly, they were at the front gate of Jessie's house.

"Coffee?" she asked.

"No, thanks, I must get back. I have a phone call to make." Bob hesitated. "You remember I mentioned visiting an old friend who runs an air photography company?"

"Yes."

"He's offered me a job. As a pilot. It would mean leaving London and finding a place somewhere around here."

Jessie felt a surge of excitement but managed to hide it. "And have you accepted?"

"No."

The excitement died. She tried to keep the disappointment from showing in her face, but he was watching her carefully.

"Should I accept?" he asked, and Jessie knew with total certainty that he was posing a quite different question.

"It's your decision," she said.

"I'm undecided," he said. "I thought you might help me make up my mind."

"You know what's best for you," she said lamely.

He nodded, his face expressionless. "I suppose so." He straightened his shoulders and forced a smile. "Well, Jessie, it was lovely meeting you again. Perhaps another time . . ."

"Yes. Thank you for dinner. Any time you're in the neighbourhood . . ."

"I will."

But she knew he would never return.

She stood at the gate and watched him walk away.

THEN she remembered the mistake she had made twenty-five years before; she remembered her bitter regrets, the thousands of times she had lain awake at nights wishing she had accepted his proposal, the thousands of times she had imagined herself running after him to tell him she had changed her mind. She drew breath to call after him, then stopped.

She couldn't do it.

She watched him until he walked out of sight, but he didn't look back. She went inside and banged the door shut and collapsed into a chair, to stare with empty eyes at the darkening sky and listen to the silence, sick with the knowledge that she had been given a second chance and had been afraid to take it.

She was still sitting there when the phone rang.

"Yes?"

"Hello, Jessie. It's Bob. I've . . ."

"Take the job!" Jessie burst out. "I mean — I think it would be a good idea if you were to take the job."

She heard his chuckle over the line. "I just did," he said.

"You already did?"

"I made a mistake twenty-five years ago," he said gently. "I should have persisted. I'm not going to make that mistake again."

Jessie struggled for words. There were so many things to say, so many things she wanted him to know, so much she wanted to hear from him.

"Come and have that coffee now," she said. "Right now!"

It seemed a perfectly reasonable way to start the rest of her life. □

IN a small flat, prettily situated in a complex of homes for the elderly, Ellie Wentworth stirred from a disturbed sleep. As always, her eyes went first to the other bed.

Her husband, Sam, was still sleeping.

Ellie moved slowly from necessity, her bones were no longer young, and quietly, because she didn't want to wake Sam. He had tossed about for most of the night.

Ellie was in the bathroom when she remembered the date. Monday, the first day of the month. With a little smile at her own foolishness she said *White Rabbits*, repeating it three times just to be sure, then made her way to the kitchen.

The early hint of October sunshine streamed into the pleasant dining area. Pulling her dressing-gown tightly round her small figure,

The Present

by MARY TEMPLE

Ellie put the kettle on, but before she could even warm the pot she heard Sam stirring.

"Now then, love," she said gently. "It's a lovely morning."

Sam nodded. Speaking didn't come easy to him now. Ellie patted his hand and reached for his clothes, neatly folded on a chair. Gently she helped him to ease himself into them. But when she came to put his arms into the smart new cardigan his niece had bought him only a month before, he shook his head.

"Your present," he told her. "Your present."

Ellie took the old, worn, Fair Isle slipover from the drawer where she had hidden it, hoping that out of sight, would, indeed be out of mind. Sam touched the faded colours and smiled as Ellie pulled it into place. Only then did he allow her to put on the smart grey cardigan. Ellie buttoned it up. The old slipover was almost hidden, but the knowledge that it was there worried the old lady.

"He'll probably remember things from the past more than recent happenings," the doctor had told her.

Ellie helped her husband into the bathroom and left him to wash his hands and face. The nurse would be in later to wash him properly. Then they sat in the sunny alcove and enjoyed tea and toast.

IT was the day for the doctor's visit and he came early.

"You know I suggested Sam going into hospital for a couple of days for some tests. Well, they think today would be best. There's nothing to worry about," he added softly, as Ellie looked at him in dismay. "We'll have him back on Wednesday, safe and sound."

He smiled.

"Now don't worry about visiting today. He'll be out of the ward most of the time. He'll be pleased to see you tomorrow afternoon."

It was the nurse who suggested taking off his woollies and putting on his dressing-gown. "Less things to worry about," she told Ellie, as the ambulance drew up.

Once she was alone, Ellie allowed herself the luxury of a few tears, but she knew she had a lot to be grateful for. She and Sam had been together now for well over fifty years. No wonder the place didn't seem like home without him.

Her eyes fell on the old slipover and she picked it up, holding it, letting her mind wander back over the past. Money had never been too plentiful. Sam had been quietly content in his work as a gardener in the local parks. He loved the earth and all growing things.

Then had come the day when they had won a weekend away. Just their names drawn out of a tub, but what a wonderful three days they had had.

That was when she had bought Sam the slipover.

How pleased he had been. Now, that weekend and the unexpected present were clearer in Sam's mind than recent happenings. He refused to be parted from it.

It was then Ellie had her idea. It was still early, she had most of the day left. Perhaps she would be successful, perhaps not, at least she could try. She was smiling as she made her way to the bus stop.

Ellie was not smiling two hours later as she stood looking up at the town's smartest shop, *Saynton's*. Dare she go in? She remembered the sniggers, the amused looks she had got in the other stores. Wearily she went into a café and had tea and a toasted tea cake. Then she held her tiny fingers erect and walked through the imposing doors.

IN a pleasant semi-detached house on the outskirts of town Julie Grantley groaned as she woke up on Monday morning to the whirring of her sister's knitting machine. Then she grinned as she saw the old toy rabbit at the bottom of her bed. Somehow it had seemed important that she remembered it was the first of the month. *White Rabbits*, she said firmly and again.

Then, as she jumped out of bed she lifted her old toy Rupert up and hugged it.

"Don't you dare let me down," she told him.

Julie was twenty, Sally, the knitting machine weilder, was twenty-three. Their older sister, Molly, had married and gone to New Zealand, where she had just presented her delighted family with a son. The proud grandparents were over there for a six-month stay, of which nearly three months had gone.

Sally had seen them off at the airport, come home, climbed on a stool to adjust a curtain hook and promptly overbalanced. The broken leg had healed, but a damaged hip was still giving trouble. Sally had, for another few weeks, to spend most of her time in a wheelchair and to say she had become bored was putting it mildly.

Hence her boyfriend's idea to present her with a knitting machine, complete with a fixture he had made that enabled her to sit in her wheelchair and use it. The idea being Sally would knit and sell jumpers for her friends.

However, Sally had found the machine decidedly unco-operative, but being a determined sort of person she had carried on trying until Julie wished the machine at the bottom of the sea.

But when Julie entered the sitting-room Sally turned to her with a beaming smile and held out several completed squares of various patterns.

"I've mastered it at last! First thing on the books today — a jumper for you."

"Oh, Sally! I'm so glad! But don't forget your exercises in all the excitement. We don't want you greeting the parents in that thing. Especially when you wouldn't tell them about the accident."

"And spoil their holiday when they'd saved all that time for it? Not likely! Anyway, Mum will probably enjoy using this as well. Now I thought you were a working girl. Looked at the time lately?"

Julie swallowed the last of her toast and dashed off, managing to walk into the men's department in *Saynton's* store at least thirty seconds before her official time.

The senior salesman, Roger Newlands, gave her a beaming smile; the floor manager, Stanley Inman, glanced at his watch and scowled.

IT was almost lunch-time when Julie looked up and saw a small, elderly lady standing hesitantly in the archway. Julie gave a spontaneous smile and the old lady promptly hurried over to her, smiled back then looked almost afraid.

"Can I help you?" Julie asked encouragingly.

"Well, I'm not sure." Slowly Ellie opened the brown paper bag and pulled out the slipover. Julie looked at it as Ellie laid it on the glass-topped counter. She saw the tender way the old fingers smoothed it out, and as she looked at her unusual customer she saw the hope filling her eyes . . .

"It's my husband's. You see, he's not well and doesn't understand. I hoped — well I wondered if you had anything a little bit like it?"

Julie was only small, but when she heard a smothered laugh she quelled the young junior with a glance.

"I'm sorry," she told Ellie.

"Oh, please! If you could just look, perhaps in the store-room? I've saved some money. Twenty pounds. You see Sam's in hospital. He's forgotten how long it is since . . ."

Her voice broke, with trembling fingers she began to fold the slipover.

Julie stopped her. "Look, I may be able to help, but I can't promise. When will your husband be home?"

"Wednesday morning."

"Then leave it with me. I'll see what I can do." Seeing Stanley Inman approaching, Julie pushed the slipover out of sight and smiled a goodbye at Ellie.

Fortunately, the clock struck the lunch-hour and Julie gave the floor manager a beaming smile as she hurried past him, the bag clutched safely in her hand. She was fully aware of his suspicious look as she went into the off-duty room. She smiled. It was not often his hawk eyes missed anything.

Julie didn't usually go home for lunch, but today she would have to. Fortunately she just managed to catch a bus and walked in as Sally was having a snack.

She stared as Julie showed her the worn, faded garment.

"Could you make one, Sally? It is important. The old lady looked so sad."

"I don't know. Fair Isle like that is rather a tall order for a beginner like me, and I'd need lots of different coloured wool."

"But Wendy at the wool shop did say she'd pop round with anything you needed," persuaded Julie. "And twenty pounds should pay for it. I know you hope to make a profit, but just this once . . ."

"All right! You win. I'll ring Wendy and see what she has. Now get some of this coffee and a sandwich. You'll make yourself ill if you

▶ over

HOLYROOD HOUSE

A CITY steeped in history, Edinburgh has so many places of interest. Holyrood Palace, situated at the end of the Royal Mile, was the Palace of our Stuart Kings and Queens.

Mary Stuart, Queen of Scots, and her son, James VI, lived here, as did Cromwell's troops.

Rizzio was murdered here — a brass tablet now marking the spot.

The name possibly derives from David I dedicating the abbey to Christ's Rood or Cross after experiencing a miraculous escape while hunting in the neighbourhood.

HOLYROOD HOUSE, EDINBURGH : J CAMPBELL KERR

start dashing home instead of having a proper lunch."

Julie laughed.

"Rubbish, you sound just like Mum." Nevertheless the plate of sandwiches was sadly depleted when she dashed off for her bus.

ON Wednesday morning Julie could scarcely contain her delight as she waited for Ellie to appear. The new slipover, in a pretty flowered bag, sat safely underneath the counter. She couldn't resist showing it to some of the girls, and when Roger Newlands came across she told him the whole story. He looked at her in a way that made her heart turn over.

"You're a kind person, Julie. I'm sure the old lady will be delighted."

Neither of them noticed Stanley Inman eyeing the proceedings with narrowed eyes and a speculative look.

It was almost ten o'clock when Julie spotted Ellie making her way slowly to the counter.

Without speaking Julie took the slipover from its hiding place and spread it on the counter. Ellie was lost for words.

"It's not quite the same," Julie admitted, "but if you think . . ."

"It's perfect. Sam will never know the difference. His mind, you know — it wanders into the past. I don't know how to thank you. Here's the twenty pounds, but if it is any more . . ."

"No, in fact," Julie pushed five pounds back into Ellie's hand, "it wasn't even that. So you and Sam can have a little treat when he comes home. Now here you are." Julie pushed the notes into her pocket and slipover into its bag.

Then, as Ellie began to walk away Stanley Inman pounced.

"Just a minute! I would like you both to come with me to the manager's office. No, Miss Grantley! It is no use arguing. I saw the transaction in the firm's time. We will see what Mr Earle has to say about it."

Julie slipped an arm round Ellie's trembling shoulders, as they were ushered into the carpeted domain of the store manager.

MR EARLE! Miss Grantley has been making private sales of menswear in the firm's time." Stanley put the slipover on to the mahogany desk and pulled himself up to his full height. "You will find the money in her pocket."

"Yes, you will!" Julie could control her temper no longer. If she was to lose her job, then she'd go down fighting.

"There it is! Fifteen pounds — the cost of the wool and I only did it because Mrs Wentworth wanted it so badly. We had nothing like it in stock and my sister is tied to the house and had just got a knitting maching . . ."

Walter Earle tapped on the desk for silence.

"Really! I can't make sense of anything. You — " He gestured towards Ellie. "You haven't said anything yet. Suppose you tell me. No, Mr Inman. I must hear both sides of the story."

He listened to Ellie's quiet explanation as she fought back the tears. "Please," Ellie finished. "I don't want Julie to lose her job. She was so kind. In the other shops the girls just laughed at me . . ."

Before the manager could speak, however, the office door burst open and the young sales manager, Roger Newlands, stormed in.

"Julie, I've just heard!"

He went across and slipped an arm round her shoulders as he faced Walter Earle.

"Please, sir! Julie did nothing wrong! She just tried to help."

"Mmm — you say your sister knitted this?" he asked Julie.

"Yes, sir."

"But — " Stanley Inman was silenced by a look from the manager's steely-grey eyes.

"Mr Inman — I think Miss Grantley used commonsense and initiative to help a customer. Now I think this office is a little overcrowded, so would you two gentlemen please leave. I would like to talk to Miss Grantley in private."

Roger gave Julie an encouraging look as he walked to the door. Stanley Inman glared.

The manager was still examining the slipover. "You know you might have something here. Young people are going for the older fashions . . ."

Outside the office Julie hugged Ellie.

"Isn't that wonderful! He wants Sally to do some samples and if they sell — well, I know Sally will be going back to work, but Mum always wanted a little job she could do at home. Come on — it's my coffee-break. To heck with the canteen, I'm going to treat you to a drink in style."

"Can anyone come," Roger Newlands asked, grinning.

"As long as it's on me — you deserve it, sticking up for me like that."

Their eyes met, and Julie turned away, blushing. Ellie gave a little knowing nod of approval, then settled to enjoy the pleasure of sitting with two young people at the beginning of a romance. If they were as happy as she and Sam had been . . .

★　　　★　　　★　　　★

Sam came home from hospital looking and speaking a little better. He pushed the cardigan aside as Ellie made to help him into it.

"No, love, this is quite warm enough." He touched the soft colours of the slipover. "You know, Ellie, it must be quite a while now since you bought me it — and it looks as good as new."

Ellie leaned over his chair and rested her cheek against his sparse white hair.

"Yes, my darling," she said gently. "As good as new." □

Printed and published in Great Britain by D. C. Thomson & Co., Ltd., Dundee, Glasgow and London. © D. C. Thomson & Co., Ltd., 1990. While every reasonable care will be taken, neither D. C. Thomson & Co., Ltd., nor its agents will accept liability for loss or damage to colour transparencies or any other material submitted to this publication.

ISBN 0-85116-488-9